Section 1 — Numbers and Arithmetic

1.1 Place Value and Ordering Numbers

Page 1   Exercise 1

1 a) i) 50   ii) 3000   iii) 200 000
   b) i) 40   ii) 2000   iii) 400 000
   c) i) 80   ii) 3000   iii) 200 000
   d) i) 60   ii) 8000   iii) 0
   e) i) 70   ii) 0   iii) 900 000
   f) i) 80   ii) 9000   iii) 300 000
   g) i) 20   ii) 2000   iii) 700 000
   h) i) 10   ii) 2000   iii) 800 000
   i) i) 0   ii) 5000   iii) 800 000
   j) i) 90   ii) 0   iii) 200 000
   k) i) 0   ii) 1000   iii) 600 000
   l) i) 30   ii) 9000   iii) 700 000

2 a) i) 30 000   ii) thirty thousand
   b) i) 8 000 000   ii) eight million
   c) i) 0   ii) zero
   d) i) 80   ii) eighty
   e) i) 3000   ii) three thousand
   f) i) 8000   ii) eight thousand
   g) i) 400 000   ii) four hundred-thousand
   h) i) 90 000   ii) ninety thousand
   i) i) 3   ii) three
   j) i) 200   ii) two hundred
   k) i) 6 000 000   ii) six million
   l) i) 50 000   ii) fifty thousand

3 a) 200, 0, 3   b) 800, 10, 0
   c) 3000, 900, 20, 1   d) 1000, 900, 80, 7
   e) 60 000, 3000, 200, 90, 1
   f) 80 000, 0, 300, 70, 3
   g) 700 000, 90 000, 7000, 600, 30, 4
   h) 20 000, 8000, 900, 70, 7
   i) 900 000, 20 000, 1000, 300, 30, 7
   j) 800 000, 10 000, 8000, 700, 50, 2
   k) 2 000 000, 800 000, 70 000, 1000, 300, 50, 4
   l) 7 000 000, 600 000, 20 000, 0, 900, 30, 1

Page 2   Exercise 2

1 a) fifteen thousand, two hundred and ninety-eight
   b) forty thousand, two hundred and ninety-one
   c) eighty-two thousand, one hundred and seventy-nine
   d) seventy-four thousand, three hundred and thirty-three
   e) twenty-three thousand and five
   f) twenty-five thousand, two hundred and twenty-one
   g) ten thousand, two hundred and eighty-one
   h) fifty-five thousand, five hundred and one

2 a) four hundred and fifty-two thousand, one hundred and twenty-three
   b) six hundred and five thousand, one hundred and twenty-eight
   c) three hundred and ninety-one thousand, four hundred and seven

   d) five hundred and [...] and ninety-eight [...]
   e) nine hundred an[...] and forty-eight
   f) two hundred and ninety-five thousand, three hundred and forty-one
   g) seven hundred and nine thousand, three hundred and eighty-two
   h) three hundred and fifty-one thousand, nine hundred and twenty-two
   i) one hundred and twenty-one thousand, four hundred and forty-five
   j) six hundred and seventy-eight thousand, one hundred and forty-four
   k) three hundred and sixty-six thousand, one hundred and twenty-one
   l) eight hundred and ninety-two thousand, one hundred and fifty-three

3 a) one million, one hundred and sixty-three thousand, seven hundred and twenty
   b) two million, eight hundred and ten thousand, two hundred and seventy-eight
   c) six millions, two hundred and one thousand, eight hundred and twenty-seven
   d) seven million, two hundred and seventy-seven thousand, two hundred and sixty
   e) six million, two hundred and seventy-one thousand and twenty-nine
   f) four million, four hundred and eighty-two thousand, nine hundred and ten
   g) one million, nine thousand, two hundred and seventy-five
   h) five million, nine hundred and ninety-seven thousand, one hundred and sixty-five
   i) one million, three hundred and twenty one thousand, nine hundred and ninety-two
   j) seven million, three hundred and ninety-two thousand and fourteen
   k) nine million, three hundred seventy-one thousand, seven hundred and twenty
   l) five million, nine thousand, eight hundred and one
   m) eight million, one hundred and nine thousand, two hundred
   n) six million, two hundred and eleven thousand, three hundred and fifteen
   o) eight million, nine hundred thousand and three
   p) one million, six hundred and twenty-eight thousand, one hundred and two

4 a) 12 397   b) 874 209   c) 6 163 511   d) 4 713 009
5 nine million, seven hundred and three thousand, one hundred and nine pounds
6 eighty eight million, six hundred thousand, five hundred and three pounds

Page 4   Exercise 3

1 a) <   b) <   c) >   d) <
   e) >   f) <   g) >   h) >
2 a) <   b) <   c) <   d) >
   e) >   f) <   g) >   h) >
   i) <   j) <   k) <   l) >

3 **a)**

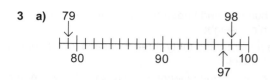

b)

c)

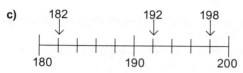

d)

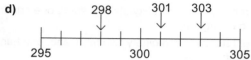

e)

4 **a)** 55, 61, 62, 67, 70, 76
b) 4, 42, 44, 56, 58, 60
c) 2, 5, 22, 25, 50, 52
d) 100, 110, 111, 112, 131, 132
e) 77, 162, 167, 172, 180, 182
f) 69, 77, 161, 171, 172, 176

5 **a)** 49, 51, 620, 621, 665, 734, 7161, 7511
b) 6, 8, 18, 84, 182, 889, 1880, 1882
c) 6, 9, 66, 68, 90, 1921, 6621, 6667
d) 3, 31, 163, 166, 168, 662, 1633, 1921

1.2 Addition and Subtraction

Page 6   Exercise 1

1 **a)** 55 **b)** 80 **c)** 65 **d)** 128
e) 129 **f)** 155 **g)** 258 **h)** 921
i) 558 **j)** 709 **k)** 1035 **l)** 865

2 **a)** 635 **b)** 908 **c)** 794 **d)** 477
e) 994 **f)** 1638 **g)** 1102 **h)** 1009

3 **a)** 9158 **b)** 6939 **c)** 8661 **d)** 7170
e) 8633 **f)** 9097 **g)** 9158 **h)** 8939
i) 9661 **j)** 12 170 **k)** 11 593 **l)** 12 097

4 **a)** 940 **b)** 893 **c)** 754 **d)** 300
e) 1590 **f)** 1834 **g)** 854 **h)** 1238
i) 3531 **j)** 8100 **k)** 7633 **l)** 8490
m) 9529 **n)** 14 223 **o)** 10 516 **p)** 12 063

5 1030

6 3353

7 £8852

8 **a)** 821 **b)** 1674 **c)** 1313 **d)** 1485
e) 3632 **f)** 2674 **g)** 4643 **h)** 9299

Page 8   Exercise 2

1 **a)** 61 **b)** 31 **c)** 11 **d)** 13
e) 451 **f)** 550 **g)** 852 **h)** 762

2 **a)** 168 **b)** 112 **c)** 158 **d)** 115
e) 70 **f)** 221 **g)** 6111 **h)** 5080
i) 7491 **j)** 3721 **k)** 6287 **l)** 8188

3 **a)** 9 **b)** 3 **c)** 56 **d)** 17
e) 381 **f)** 456 **g)** 308 **h)** 581
i) 569 **j)** 98 **k)** 195 **l)** 284
m) 3237 **n)** 1076 **o)** 4109 **p)** 4614
q) 6920 **r)** 2669 **s)** 7722 **t)** 6081

4 **a)** 54 **b)** 172 **c)** 905 **d)** 8091

5 787

6 45

7 1751

8 7131

9 7808

10 5588

Page 10   Exercise 3

1 **a)** 6.7 **b)** 9.9 **c)** 6.2 **d)** 5.5
e) 7.1 **f)** 9.92 **g)** 10.94 **h)** 12.17
i) 9.19 **j)** 12.98

2 **a)** 11.57 **b)** 8.56 **c)** 14.24 **d)** 1.32
e) 13.394 **f)** 13.659 **g)** 7.086 **h)** 12.476

3 **a)** 9.997 **b)** 10.984 **c)** 11.234
d) 12.005 **e)** 12.719

4 **a)** 9.66 **b)** 8.67 **c)** 8.85 **d)** 13.16
e) 10.32 **f)** 15.07 **g)** 18.43 **h)** 12.02
i) 14.378 **j)** 10.862 **k)** 7.879 **l)** 8.270

5 **a)** 9.189 **b)** 51.1 **c)** 21.22

6 £2.75

7 £48.07

8 29.16 km

9 **a)** £7.12 **b)** £6.91 **c)** £12.01
d) £7.30 **e)** £6.86 **f)** £6.27

Page 12   Exercise 4

1 **a)** 2.7 **b)** 4.1 **c)** 5.9 **d)** 3.8
e) 1.9 **f)** 1.14 **g)** 1.98 **h)** 7.51
i) 8.19 **j)** 4.22 **k)** 2.62 **l)** 0.66
m) 1.75 **n)** 1.41 **o)** 3.29 **p)** 12.24
q) 25.79 **r)** 37.32 **s)** 21.06 **t)** 4.69

2 **a)** 2.582 **b)** 2.371 **c)** 5.159 **d)** 1.257
e) 2.229 **f)** 4.922 **g)** 1.929 **h)** 2.008
i) 4.211 **j)** 1.089 **k)** 3.194 **l)** 1.815

3 **a)** 1.1 **b)** 0.8 **c)** 3.3 **d)** 1.4
e) 14.7 **f)** 86.6 **g)** 64.1 **h)** 14.7
i) 1.05 **j)** 0.3 **k)** 2.77 **l)** 3.79
m) 83.74 **n)** 87.21 **o)** 16.05 **p)** 39.43
q) 2.27 **r)** 2.114 **s)** 2.609 **t)** 2.915

4 **a)** 6.571 **b)** 1.226 **c)** 39.28 **d)** 6.091

5 £2.11

6 59.09 km

7 £29.18

8 £17.80

Page 15 Exercise 1

1 a) 60   b) 40   c) 90   d) 710
   e) 630   f) 500   g) 2690   h) 4800
   i) 2270   j) 3130

2 a) 500   b) 900   c) 100   d) 300
   e) 3100   f) 8800   g) 4500   h) 1600
   i) 78 000 j) 28 900 k) 62 100 l) 88 600

3 a) 8000   b) 3000   c) 7000
   d) 9000   e) 63 000   f) 90 000
   g) 21 000   h) 52 000   i) 341 000
   j) 400 000   k) 942 000   l) 186 000

4 a) 600   b) 820   c) 6810   d) 71 200
   e) 20   f) 821 000 g) 71 000 h) 90 000

5 a) 1600   b) 1800   c) 3500
   d) 12 000   e) 4000   f) 30 000
   g) 240 000   h) 250 000   i) 60 000
   j) 80 000   k) 4 200 000   l) 1 600 000
   m) 2 000 000   n) 42 000 000 o) 18 000 000
   p) 24 000 000

6 a) 50   b) 10   c) 1000
   d) 100   e) 50   f) 600
   g) 20   h) 400   i) 90

Page 16 Exercise 2

1 a) 4   b) 5   c) 2
   d) 7   e) 9   f) 50
   g) 28   h) 69   i) 43
   j) 37   k) 570   l) 400
   m) 435   n) 3180   o) 8307

2 a) 4   b) 5   c) 8   d) 9
   e) 7   f) 82   g) 77   h) 10
   i) 67   j) 39   k) 570   l) 465

3 a) 9   b) 3   c) 5   d) 7
   e) 16   f) 82   g) 10   h) 55
   i) 657   j) 490   k) 200   l) 312

4 a) 4.5   b) 5.2   c) 2.8   d) 71.5
   e) 52.3   f) 30.9   g) 818.2   h) 434.4
   i) 4.9   j) 5.8   k) 2.3   l) 8.7
   m) 57.2   n) 43.2   o) 953.1   p) 761.7
   q) 4.3   r) 5.9   s) 23.1   t) 79.6
   u) 59.8   v) 276.4   w) 248.7   x) 404.5

5 a) 0.42   b) 0.58   c) 2.73   d) 7.34
   e) 53.31   f) 28.92   g) 7.43   h) 1.09
   i) 40.32   j) 87.25   k) 254.98 l) 742.21

6 675 g

7 0.57 litres

Page 19 Exercise 3

1 | 70 × 8 = 560 | 2 × 8 = 16 |
   |---|---|

   576

2 | 800 × 9 = 7200 | 20 × 9 = 180 | 6 × 9 = 54 |
   |---|---|---|

   7434

3 | 700 × 30 = 21 000 | 30 × 30 = 900 | 1 × 30 = 30 |
   |---|---|---|
   | 700 × 8 = 5600 | 30 × 8 = 240 | 1 × 8 = 8 |

   27 778

4 a) 280   b) 376   c) 354   d) 448
   e) 4823   f) 3240   g) 10 503 h) 35 972
   i) 2112   j) 38 496

5 a) 208   b) 415   c) 455   d) 552
   e) 136   f) 171   g) 612   h) 184
   i) 616   j) 280

6 a) 2772   b) 552   c) 2752   d) 544
   e) 2241   f) 2784   g) 3724   h) 6192
   i) 2277   j) 1705

7 a) 19 642 b) 9553   c) 54 694 d) 34 503
   e) 20 539 f) 32 414 g) 19 008 h) 3318
   i) 9476   j) 22 199

8 a) 99 696 b) 475 044 c) 314 112 d) 640 953
   e) 322 270 f) 148 342 g) 334 872 h) 650 085
   i) 460 428 j) 598 552 k) 395 240 l) 396 912
   m) 527 560 n) 464 802 o) 92 378 p) 234 320

9 608

10 3136

11 a) £234   b) £156   c) £312   d) £546
    e) £1638 f) £1144   g) £858   h) £2132

12 1068 kg

13 £1806

14 a) 880   b) 1408   c) 1584   d) 704
    e) 2464   f) 5632   g) 4752   h) 10 912

15 £37 812

16 a) 988   b) 1924   c) 2548   d) 4576
    e) 6812   f) 41 808 g) 19 864 h) 15 080

17 £35 996

18 £21 948

19 152 964 km

20 a) 4750 ml   b) 16 625 ml   c) 11 875 ml
    d) 14 250 ml   e) 30 875 ml   f) 104 500 ml
    g) 171 000 ml   h) 125 875 ml

21 222 404

Page 22 Exercise 4

1 a) 14   b) 23   c) 15   d) 13   e) 26
   f) 48   g) 9   h) 12   i) 29   j) 18

2 a) 24 r 1   b) 19 r 2   c) 15 r 3
   d) 43 r 1   e) 6 r 1   f) 13 r 2
   g) 22 r 3   h) 13 r 4   i) 12 r 3
   j) 21 r 2   k) 13 r 4   l) 29 r 2
   m) 13 r 3   n) 12 r 4   o) 22 r 1

3 a) 96   b) 63   c) 114   d) 231
   e) 89   f) 51   g) 32   h) 32
   i) 61   j) 24   k) 21   l) 12

4 a) 54 r 4   b) 155 r 1   c) 180 r 3   d) 41 r 1
   e) 131 r 5 f) 48 r 6   g) 40 r 5   h) 13 r 4
   i) 63 r 1   j) 22 r 12   k) 23 r 2   l) 46 r 3

5 a) 253   b) 651   c) 1546   d) 951
   e) 1103   f) 726   g) 321   h) 221
   i) 212   j) 421   k) 541   l) 422

6 a) 152 r 6   **b)** 1894 r 1   **c)** 812 r 3   **d)** 927 r 5
   e) 653 r 12   **f)** 231 r 15   **g)** 483 r 6   **h)** 617 r 1

7 a) 16   **b)** 14   **c)** 34
   d) 127   **e)** 41   **f)** 62
   g) 24   **h)** 32   **i)** 51
   j) 154   **k)** 472   **l)** 635
   m) 443   **n)** 321   **o)** 402

8 a) 9 r 2   **b)** 15 r 2   **c)** 14 r 4
   d) 19 r 4   **e)** 66 r 3   **f)** 59 r 1
   g) 51 r 6   **h)** 38 r 8   **i)** 64 r 7
   j) 245 r 6   **k)** 561 r 4   **l)** 941 r 4
   m) 156 r 8   **n)** 234 r 2   **o)** 206 r 2

9 a) 618   **b)** 209

10 £156

11 46

12 11

1.4 Calculations with Negative Numbers

Page 25   Exercise 1

1 a) 2   **b)** 4   **c)** −3   **d)** 3
   e) −8   **f)** 12   **g)** 17   **h)** −2
   i) 3   **j)** 16   **k)** 4   **l)** −9
   m) −2   **n)** −18   **o)** 9   **p)** 1

2 a) −6   **b)** −4   **c)** −11   **d)** −4
   e) −5   **f)** −7   **g)** −25   **h)** −14
   i) −8   **j)** −8   **k)** −6   **l)** −9
   m) −8   **n)** −11   **o)** −6   **p)** −9

3 a) −12   **b)** −14   **c)** −10   **d)** −19
   e) −18   **f)** −27   **g)** −31   **h)** −43
   i) −29   **j)** −36   **k)** −44   **l)** −53

4 a) 26 °C   **b)** 39 °C   **c)** 42 °C   **d)** 29 °C

5 9 metres

6 a) £99   **b)** £46

1.5 Calculators, BODMAS and Checking

Page 28   Exercise 1

1 a) multiplication, addition
   b) division, subtraction
   c) multiplication, subtraction
   d) division, subtraction
   e) division, subtraction, addition,
   f) multiplication, division, subtraction
   g) multiplication, addition, subtraction
   h) division, multiplication, addition

2 a) 9   **b)** 11   **c)** 38   **d)** 17
   e) 14   **f)** 73   **g)** 66   **h)** 31
   i) 6   **j)** 17   **k)** 20   **l)** 21

3 a) 18   **b)** 12   **c)** 121
   d) 56   **e)** 42   **f)** 12
   g) 12   **h)** 22   **i)** 100
   j) 33   **k)** 45   **l)** 63
   m) 11   **n)** 8   **o)** 11

4 a) 56   **b)** 38   **c)** 29   **d)** 10
   e) 4   **f)** 34   **g)** 75   **h)** 48
   i) 84   **j)** 7   **k)** 46   **l)** 132

5 a) 17   **b)** 14   **c)** 24   **d)** 43
   e) 21   **f)** 11   **g)** 38   **h)** 66
   i) 33   **j)** 20   **k)** 5   **l)** 8

6 a) 4   **b)** 17   **c)** 72
   d) 59   **e)** 72   **f)** 30
   g) 36   **h)** 49   **i)** 37

Page 30   Exercise 2

1 a) $(10 \div 2) + 3 = 8$ $10 \div (3 + 2) = 2$
   b) $(3 \times 7) − 4 = 17$ $3 \times (7 − 4) = 9$
   c) $(3 \times 4) + 6 = 18$ $3 \times (4 + 6) = 30$
   d) $(12 \div 3) \times 2 = 8$ $12 \div (3 \times 2) = 2$
   e) $(60 + 12) \div 6 = 12$ $60 + (12 \div 6) = 62$
   f) $(24 + 12) \div 6 = 6$ $24 + (12 \div 6) = 26$
   g) $(10 \times 2) + 11 = 31$ $10 \times (2 + 11) = 130$
   h) $(25 − 8) \times 3 = 51$ $25 − (8 \times 3) = 1$
   i) $(7 + 2) \times 9 = 81$ $7 + (2 \times 9) = 25$
   j) $(40 − 36) \div 4 = 1$ $40 − (36 \div 4) = 31$
   k) $(84 \div 7) + 5 = 17$ $84 \div (7 + 5) = 7$
   l) $(27 − 9) \div 9 = 2$ $27 − (9 \div 9) = 26$

2 a) $16 \div (8 \times 2) = 1$ **b)** $60 \div (5 + 5) = 6$
   c) $(8 − 6) \times 12 = 24$ **d)** $(14 − 2) \times 6 = 72$
   e) $(6 + 3) \times 4 = 36$ **f)** $(4 + 2) \times 7 = 42$
   g) $(88 + 55) \div 11 = 13$ **h)** $(60 + 10) \div 7 = 10$
   i) $(42 + 3) \div 9 = 5$ **j)** $(8 − 1) \times 9 = 63$
   k) $36 \div (3 + 3) = 6$ **l)** $(22 − 7) \times 2 = 30$
   m) $4 \times (10 + 2) = 48$ **n)** $(150 − 6) \div 12 = 12$
   o) $(50 − 2) \div 6 = 8$

3 a) BODMAS tells us that the division is done before the addition. $52 \div 2 + 2 = 28$
   b) $52 \div (2 + 2) = 13$

4 a) $3 + 5 \times (6 − 2) = 23$ **b)** $(8 − 2) \times 4 + 8 = 32$
   c) $40 \div (8 \div 2) \times 11 = 110$ **d)** $9 + 1 − (10 − 2) = 2$
   e) $9 \times (6 + 3) − 7 = 74$ **f)** $99 \div (12 − 3) + 11 = 22$
   g) $(15 − 12) \times 3 \times 12 = 108$ **h)** $(11 − 9 + 2) \times 11 = 44$

5 a) Paul has not used BODMAS and worked the calculation out from left to right. $3 \times 10 + 9 \div 3 = 33$
   b) $3 \times (10 + 9) \div 3 = 19$.

Page 31   Exercise 3

1 a) $27 − 8 = 19$ or $27 − 19 = 8$
   b) $17 − 11 = 6$ or $17 − 6 = 11$
   c) $7 + 14 = 21$ or $14 + 7 = 21$
   d) $20 + 22 = 42$ or $22 + 20 = 42$
   e) $6 + 9 = 15$ or $9 + 6 = 15$
   f) $25 − 18 = 7$ or $25 − 7 = 18$
   g) $9 + 15 = 24$ or $15 + 9 = 24$
   h) $27 − 11 = 16$ or $27 − 16 = 11$
   i) $5 + 17 = 22$ or $17 + 5 = 22$
   j) $34 − 19 = 15$ or $34 − 15 = 19$
   k) $17 + 22 = 39$ or $22 + 17 = 39$
   l) $37 − 12 = 25$ or $37 − 25 = 12$
   m) $21 + 10 = 31$ or $10 + 21 = 31$
   n) $18 + 4 = 22$ or $4 + 18 = 22$
   o) $42 − 14 = 28$ or $42 − 28 = 14$
   p) $39 − 29 = 10$ or $39 − 10 = 29$

2 a) $25 \div 5 = 5$
  b) $12 \div 3 = 4$ or $12 \div 4 = 3$
  c) $7 \times 6 = 42$ or $6 \times 7 = 42$
  d) $9 \times 8 = 72$ or $8 \times 9 = 72$
  e) $32 \div 4 = 8$ or $32 \div 8 = 4$
  f) $21 \div 3 = 7$ or $21 \div 7 = 3$
  g) $50 \div 10 = 5$ or $50 \div 5 = 10$
  h) $2 \times 9 = 18$ or $9 \times 2 = 18$
  i) $9 \times 10 = 90$ or $10 \times 9 = 90$
  j) $2 \times 6 = 12$ or $6 \times 2 = 12$
  k) $11 \times 11 = 121$
  l) $12 \times 8 = 96$ or $8 \times 12 = 96$
  m) $7 \times 9 = 63$ or $9 \times 7 = 63$
  n) $64 \div 8 = 8$
  o) $77 \div 11 = 7$ or $77 \div 7 = 11$
  p) $132 \div 12 = 11$ or $132 \div 11 = 12$

Section 2 — Approximations

2.1 Rounding

Page 32   Exercise 1

1 a) 30   **b)** 70   **c)** 30   **d)** 10
  e) 50   **f)** 10   **g)** 60   **h)** 60
  i) 120   **j)** 320   **k)** 400   **l)** 590
2 a) 300   **b)** 400   **c)** 300   **d)** 700
  e) 500   **f)** 900   **g)** 400   **h)** 700
  i) 1200   **j)** 2400   **k)** 4600   **l)** 5300
3 a) 1000   **b)** 7000   **c)** 5000   **d)** 3000
  e) 1000   **f)** 5000   **g)** 7000   **h)** 5000
  i) 2000   **j)** 1000
4 a) 12 000 **b)** 16 000 **c)** 28 000 **d)** 33 000
  e) 99 000 **f)** 60 000 **g)** 18 000 **h)** 38 000
  i) 47 000 **j)** 51 000
5 a) 5270   **b)** 5300   **c)** 5000
6 a) 7850   **b)** 7900   **c)** 8000
7 15 000
8 245, 246, 247, 248, 249
9 351, 352, 353, 354
10 a) 9000   **b)** 9000   **c)** 9000
11 150
12 23 499

Page 35   Exercise 2

1 a) 4   **b)** 9   **c)** 2   **d)** 7
  e) 2   **f)** 8   **g)** 11   **h)** 19
  i) 29   **j)** 45   **k)** 109   **l)** 30
2 5.2, 4.6, 5.3, 4.9, 4.5
3 a) 6   **b)** 9   **c)** 2   **d)** 7
  e) 6   **f)** 18   **g)** 1   **h)** 8
  i) 19   **j)** 25   **k)** 91   **l)** 10
4 12.15, 11.65, 12.06, 12.29, 11.87
5 3.1, 3.2, 3.3 or 3.4
6 10.50, 10.51, 10.52, 10.53, 10.54, ... , 10.98 or 10.99

7 Any 5 decimals from 14.5 to 15.5 (not including 15.5).
8 7.5 cm
9 0.5

2.2 Estimating

Page 36   Exercise 1

1 a) 300 and 200   **b)** 500
2 a) 500 and 200   **b)** 300
3 a) 800 and 500   **b)** 300
4 a) 60 and 10   **b)** 6
5 a) 30 and 10   **b)** 300
6 680
7 490
8 400
9 1000
10 5
11 3

You might get slightly different answers to questions 12-13 and 16-20 if you round differently.

12 a) 870   **b)** 380   **c)** 400
   d) 600   **e)** 600   **f)** 800
   g) 1300   **h)** 10   **i)** 4
   j) 10   **k)** 6   **l)** 5
13 400
14 a) 50 and 5   **b)** 10
15 a) 300 and 6   **b)** 1800
16 a) 160   **b)** 90   **c)** 400
   d) 10   **e)** 30   **f)** 8
17 100 cm
18 8 cm
19 £200
20 10p

Section 3 — Powers

3.1 Powers

Page 39   Exercise 1

1 a) $5^2 = 5 \times 5 = 25$ **b)** $2^2 = 2 \times 2 = 4$
  c) $6^2 = 6 \times 6 = 36$ **d)** $4^2 = 4 \times 4 = 16$

2

a	1	7	8	9	10
a^2	1	49	64	81	100

3 a) 144   **b)** 225   **c)** 121
  d) 169   **e)** 1600   **f)** 1225
  g) 3600   **h)** 2500   **i)** 10 000
4 a) i) $(-2) \times (-2)$ **ii)** 4
  b) i) $(-5) \times (-5)$ **ii)** 25
  c) i) $(-10) \times (-10)$ **ii)** 100
  d) i) $(-6) \times (-6)$ **ii)** 36
  e) i) $(-13) \times (-13)$ **ii)** 169
  f) i) 0.1×0.1 **ii)** 0.01

g) i) 0.6 × 0.6   ii) 0.36
h) i) 0.4 × 0.4   ii) 0.16
i) i) 1.5 × 1.5   ii) 2.25
j) i) (−0.1) × (−0.1)   ii) 0.01
k) i) (−0.5) × (−0.5)   ii) 0.25
l) i) (−1.4) × (−1.4)   ii) 1.96

Page 41   Exercise 2

1 a) $2^3 = 2 × 2 × 2 = 8$
  b) $6^3 = 6 × 6 × 6 = 216$
  c) $5^3 = 5 × 5 × 5 = 125$

2

a	1	3	4	8	10
a^3	1	27	64	512	1000

3 a) 343   b) 1728   c) 1331
  d) 729   e) 2197   f) 5832
  g) 8000   h) 3375   i) 27 000

4 a) i) (−2) × (−2) × (−2)   ii) −8
  b) i) (−6) × (−6) × (−6)   ii) −216
  c) i) (−12) × (−12) × (−12)   ii) −1728
  d) i) (−5) × (−5) × (−5)   ii) −125
  e) i) (−10) × (−10) × (−10)   ii) −1000
  f) i) 0.5 × 0.5 × 0.5   ii) 0.125
  g) i) 0.4 × 0.4 × 0.4   ii) 0.064
  h) i) 1.6 × 1.6 × 1.6   ii) 4.096
  i) i) (−0.2) × (−0.2) × (−0.2)   ii) −0.008
  j) i) (−0.1) × (−0.1) × (−0.1)   ii) −0.001
  k) i) (−0.3) × (−0.3) × (−0.3)   ii) −0.027
  l) i) (−4.5) × (−4.5) × (−4.5)   ii) −91.125

3.2 Roots

Page 43   Exercise 1

1 a) $4 = 2 × 2$. So $\sqrt{4} = 2$ and $-\sqrt{4} = -2$
  b) $9 = 3 × 3$. So $\sqrt{9} = 3$ and $-\sqrt{9} = -3$

2

x	16	25	36	81	100
$\sqrt{x}$	4	5	6	9	10
$-\sqrt{x}$	−4	−5	−6	−9	−10

3 a) 5   b) −5   c) 8   d) −8
  e) 11   f) −11   g) 12   h) −12
4 a) 16 and −16   b) 19 and −19
  c) 20 and −20   d) 100 and −100
  e) 15 and −15   f) 25 and −25
  g) 18 and −18   h) 14 and −14
5 a) 0.6 and −0.6   b) 1.6 and −1.6
  c) 0.9 and −0.9   d) 0.5 and −0.5
  e) 1.3 and −1.3   f) 4.1 and −4.1

Section 4 — Multiples, Factors and Primes

4.1 Multiples

Page 44   Exercise 1

1 a) 2, 4, 6, 8, 10   b) 5, 10, 15, 20, 25
  c) 7, 14, 21, 28, 35   d) 9, 18, 27, 36, 45
  e) 8, 16, 24, 32, 40   f) 11, 22, 33, 44, 55
2 a) 36, 18, 24, 12, 30   b) 24, 16, 32, 40
3 12, 24, 36, 48
4 36, 45, 54
5 a) 33   b) 21, 28, 35, 42, 49   c) 56
6 a) 12, 14, 16, 18, 20, 22, 24
  b) 12, 15, 18, 21, 24
  c) 12, 18, 24
7 22, 17, 23, 65, 77, 49

Page 46   Exercise 2

1 a) 2, 4, 6, 8, 10, 12, 14, 16, 18, 20
  b) 3, 6, 9, 12, 15, 18, 21, 24, 27, 30
  c) 6, 12, 18
  d) 6
2 a) 4, 8, 12, 16, 20, 24, 28, 32
  b) 7, 14, 21, 28, 35, 42, 49, 56
  c) 28
3 a) 6, 12, 18, 24, 30
  b) 9, 18, 27, 36, 45
  c) 18
4 a) 15   b) 14   c) 20
  d) 45   e) 21   f) 72

4.2 Factors

Page 47   Exercise 1

1 a) 3 × 5
    4 × —
  b) 3 × 8
    4 × 6
    5 × —
2 a) 1, 2, 5   b) 1   c) 1, 2, 5
  d) 1, 2, 4, 7   e) 1, 2   f) 1, 2, 4, 8
3 1, 3, 9
4 1, 3, 7, 21
5 a) 1, 7   b) 1, 5, 25
  c) 1, 2, 4, 8, 16   d) 1, 3, 5, 9, 15, 45
  e) 1, 2, 4, 8, 16, 32, 64
  f) 1, 2, 3, 4, 6, 8, 12, 16, 24, 48
6 a) 2, 4   b) 3

Page 49   Exercise 2

1 a) 1, 2, 3, 6
  b) 1, 2, 3, 4, 6, 8, 12, 24
  c) 1, 2, 3, 6
  d) 6
2 a) 1, 2, 5, 10   b) 1, 3, 5, 15   c) 5
3 a) 1, 2, 3, 4, 6, 12   b) 1, 5, 25   c) 1

4 **a)** 4 **b)** 8 **c)** 7
 d) 5 **e)** 6 **f)** 10
5 **a)** 1 **b)** 1 **c)** 1
 d) 1 **e)** 1 **f)** 1
6 **a)** 4 **b)** 2 **c)** 10
 d) 7 **e)** 3 **f)** 8

4.3 Prime Numbers

Page 50   Exercise 1

1 **a)** Factors of 30: 1, 2, 3, 5, 6, 10, 15, 30
 Factors of 31: 1, 31
 Factors of 32: 1, 2, 4, 8, 16, 32

 b) 31 is a prime number as its only factors are itself and 1.

2 **a)** 45

 b) 45 = 5 × 9, so it is not prime (it has factors other than itself and 1).

3 **a)** 21, 25 and 27

 b) 21 = 3 × 7, 25 = 5 × 5 and 27 = 3 × 9 — they all have factors other than themselves and 1, so are not prime.

4 7, 23, 53, 59

5 **a)** 11, 13, 17, 19 **b)** 31, 37

6 **a)** 67 **b)** 41, 43, 47

7 42 = 6 × 7, so it has factors other than itself and 1.

8 The only factors of 41 are 1 and 41, so it is prime.

9 No, 51 is not prime, as 51 = 3 × 17 — so it has factors other than itself and 1.

10 71, 73, 79

Section 5 — Fractions and Percentages

5.1 Equivalent Fractions

Page 52   Exercise 1

1 **a)** $\frac{1}{6}$ **b)** $\frac{5}{8}$ **c)** $\frac{7}{10}$

 d) $\frac{3}{10}$ **e)** $\frac{11}{20}$ **f)** $\frac{14}{25}$

2 **a)** E.g.

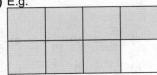

 b) E.g.

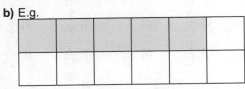

 c) E.g.

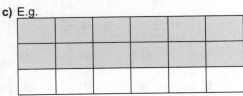

 d) E.g.

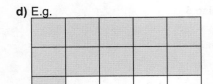

Page 54   Exercise 2

1 **a)** $\frac{1}{4}$ and $\frac{4}{16}$ **b)** $\frac{6}{12}$ and $\frac{2}{4}$

 c) $\frac{6}{24}$ and $\frac{4}{16}$ **d)** $\frac{16}{32}$ and $\frac{6}{12}$

2 **a) i)** E.g.

 ii) $a = 2$, $b = 4$

 b) i) E.g.

 ii) $c = 6$, $d = 12$

3 **a) i)** $\frac{2}{3}, \frac{6}{9}$ **ii)** equivalent

 b) i) $\frac{1}{3}, \frac{4}{6}$ **ii)** not equivalent

 c) i) $\frac{4}{12}, \frac{1}{4}$ **ii)** not equivalent

 d) i) $\frac{3}{4}, \frac{12}{16}$ **ii)** equivalent

Page 55   Exercise 3

1 **a)** 4 **b)** 2 **c)** 10 **d)** 8
 e) 3 **f)** 4 **g)** 2 **h)** 3
2 **a)** 10 **b)** 12 **c)** 25 **d)** 35
 e) 27 **f)** 7 **g)** 4 **h)** 8
3 **a)** $a = 6$, $b = 12$ **b)** $a = 6$, $b = 6$
 c) $a = 8$, $b = 6$ **d)** $a = 5$, $b = 12$

Page 57   Exercise 4

1 **a)** ■ = 4 **b)** ■ = 10, ● = 3 **c)** ■ = 3, ● = 3

2 **a)** 3 **b)** $\frac{1}{3}$

3 **a)** 7 **b)** $\frac{3}{4}$

4 **a)** ✸ = 10, ☾ = 5 **b)** ✸ = 15, ▲ = 2, ☾ = 5
 c) ✸ = 6, ▲ = 3, ☾ = 4 **d)** ✸ = 18, ▲ = 6, ☾ = 7

5 **a)** $\frac{1}{2}$ **b)** $\frac{1}{4}$ **c)** $\frac{1}{4}$ **d)** $\frac{4}{5}$ **e)** $\frac{1}{10}$ **f)** $\frac{1}{3}$
 g) $\frac{1}{10}$ **h)** $\frac{4}{13}$ **i)** $\frac{1}{2}$ **j)** $\frac{2}{3}$ **k)** $\frac{2}{3}$ **l)** $\frac{2}{3}$
 m) $\frac{5}{9}$ **n)** $\frac{5}{8}$ **o)** $\frac{3}{4}$ **p)** $\frac{3}{7}$ **q)** $\frac{2}{3}$ **r)** $\frac{6}{7}$

6 **a)** $\frac{7}{8}$ **b)** $\frac{5}{14}$ **c)** $\frac{1}{3}$ **d)** $\frac{1}{4}$ **e)** $\frac{191}{1000}$ **f)** $\frac{5}{9}$
 g) $\frac{2}{7}$ **h)** $\frac{4}{9}$ **i)** $\frac{3}{5}$ **j)** $\frac{7}{11}$ **k)** $\frac{5}{12}$ **l)** $\frac{9}{13}$

1 $\frac{4}{6}, \frac{1}{6}$

2 $\frac{6}{10}, \frac{9}{10}$

3 E.g. **a)** 8   **b)** $\frac{4}{8}, \frac{3}{8}$

4 E.g. **a)** $\frac{6}{8}, \frac{3}{8}$ **b)** $\frac{3}{12}, \frac{7}{12}$ **c)** $\frac{3}{15}, \frac{11}{15}$ **d)** $\frac{8}{10}, \frac{3}{10}$

   e) $\frac{5}{6}, \frac{2}{6}$ **f)** $\frac{10}{15}, \frac{3}{15}$ **g)** $\frac{16}{20}, \frac{7}{20}$ **h)** $\frac{15}{18}, \frac{13}{18}$

   i) $\frac{6}{24}, \frac{17}{24}$ **j)** $\frac{17}{18}, \frac{8}{18}$ **k)** $\frac{21}{28}, \frac{8}{28}$ **l)** $\frac{12}{25}, \frac{15}{25}$

   m) $\frac{16}{40}, \frac{15}{40}$ **n)** $\frac{11}{30}, \frac{9}{30}$ **o)** $\frac{19}{42}, \frac{24}{42}$ **p)** $\frac{35}{56}, \frac{37}{56}$

5 $\frac{4}{12}, \frac{9}{12}$

6 $\frac{15}{18}, \frac{14}{18}$

7 E.g. **a)** 15   **b)** $\frac{10}{15}, \frac{12}{15}$

8 E.g. **a)** 22   **b)** $\frac{11}{22}, \frac{10}{22}$

9 E.g. **a)** $\frac{3}{6}, \frac{4}{6}$ **b)** $\frac{9}{12}, \frac{8}{12}$ **c)** $\frac{16}{24}, \frac{15}{24}$

   d) $\frac{10}{12}, \frac{3}{12}$ **e)** $\frac{9}{72}, \frac{56}{72}$ **f)** $\frac{28}{35}, \frac{15}{35}$

   g) $\frac{30}{33}, \frac{11}{33}$ **h)** $\frac{21}{30}, \frac{18}{30}$ **i)** $\frac{6}{42}, \frac{35}{42}$

10 **a)** $\frac{12}{24}$ **b)** $\frac{20}{24}$ **c)** $\frac{12}{24}, \frac{20}{24}, \frac{19}{24}$

11 **a)** $\frac{15}{18}$ **b)** $\frac{4}{18}$ **c)** $\frac{15}{18}, \frac{4}{18}, \frac{3}{18}$

12 E.g. **a)** $\frac{5}{15}, \frac{6}{15}, \frac{9}{15}$ **b)** $\frac{8}{16}, \frac{12}{16}, \frac{7}{16}$ **c)** $\frac{15}{20}, \frac{12}{20}, \frac{17}{20}$

   d) $\frac{8}{24}, \frac{21}{24}, \frac{21}{24}$ **e)** $\frac{9}{21}, \frac{14}{21}, \frac{12}{21}$ **f)** $\frac{20}{28}, \frac{21}{28}, \frac{5}{28}$

   g) $\frac{28}{35}, \frac{30}{35}, \frac{20}{35}$ **h)** $\frac{36}{40}, \frac{24}{40}, \frac{33}{40}$ **i)** $\frac{7}{42}, \frac{29}{42}, \frac{30}{42}$

13 E.g. **a)** $\frac{16}{36}, \frac{21}{36}, \frac{30}{36}$ **b)** $\frac{15}{48}, \frac{18}{48}, \frac{28}{48}$

1

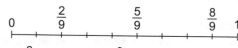

2 **a)** $\frac{8}{12}$ **b)** $\frac{9}{12}$

3 **a)** $\frac{24}{32}, \frac{27}{32}$ **b)** $\frac{27}{32}$

4 **a)** $\frac{5}{15}, \frac{9}{15}$ **b)** $\frac{4}{15}, \frac{1}{3}, \frac{3}{5}$

5 **a)** $\frac{10}{12}, \frac{3}{12}$ **b)** $\frac{2}{12}, \frac{1}{4}, \frac{5}{6}$

6 **a)** $\frac{7}{20}, \frac{1}{2}, \frac{3}{5}$ **b)** $\frac{2}{5}, \frac{11}{20}, \frac{7}{10}$

   c) $\frac{1}{4}, \frac{13}{20}, \frac{4}{5}$ **d)** $\frac{3}{20}, \frac{1}{2}, \frac{7}{10}$

7 **a)** $\frac{1}{3}, \frac{7}{18}, \frac{5}{9}$ **b)** $\frac{4}{9}, \frac{11}{18}, \frac{5}{6}$

   c) $\frac{7}{18}, \frac{1}{2}, \frac{5}{6}, \frac{8}{9}$ **d)** $\frac{1}{6}, \frac{4}{9}, \frac{2}{3}, \frac{13}{18}$

8 **a)** $\frac{5}{8}, \frac{11}{16}, \frac{3}{4}$ **b)** $\frac{1}{6}, \frac{5}{24}, \frac{7}{8}$ **c)** $\frac{4}{15}, \frac{19}{30}, \frac{5}{6}$

   d) $\frac{4}{16}, \frac{5}{16}, \frac{3}{8}, \frac{1}{2}$ **e)** $\frac{2}{4}, \frac{5}{7}, \frac{3}{4}, \frac{23}{28}$ **f)** $\frac{3}{16}, \frac{15}{32}, \frac{5}{8}, \frac{24}{32}$

9 **a) i)** $\frac{1}{15}, \frac{3}{15}, \frac{1}{3}, \frac{2}{5}, \frac{3}{5}$

   ii)

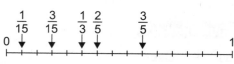

   b) i) $\frac{1}{3}, \frac{5}{8}, \frac{2}{3}, \frac{17}{24}, \frac{20}{24}$

   ii)

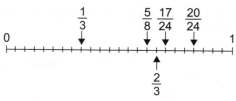

   c) i) $\frac{1}{4}, \frac{4}{8}, \frac{11}{16}, \frac{3}{4}, \frac{7}{8}$

   ii)

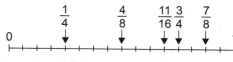

   d) i) $\frac{1}{4}, \frac{6}{10}, \frac{13}{20}, \frac{7}{10}, \frac{3}{4}$

   ii)

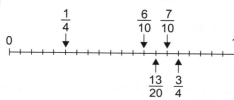

5.2 Adding and Subtracting Fractions

1 **a)** $\frac{2}{9} + \frac{2}{9} = \frac{2+2}{9} = \frac{4}{9}$

   b) $\frac{5}{8} + \frac{2}{8} = \frac{5+2}{8} = \frac{7}{8}$

   c) $\frac{6}{7} - \frac{3}{7} = \frac{6-3}{7} = \frac{3}{7}$

2 **a)** $\frac{5}{8}$ **b)** $\frac{6}{7}$ **c)** $\frac{10}{11}$ **d)** $\frac{7}{10}$ **e)** $\frac{5}{6}$

   f) $\frac{7}{12}$ **g)** $\frac{11}{13}$ **h)** $\frac{8}{13}$ **i)** $\frac{15}{16}$ **j)** $\frac{17}{21}$

3 **a)** $\frac{1}{9}$ **b)** $\frac{3}{13}$ **c)** $\frac{2}{5}$ **d)** $\frac{3}{7}$ **e)** $\frac{1}{8}$

   f) $\frac{7}{15}$ **g)** $\frac{9}{16}$ **h)** $\frac{1}{13}$ **i)** $\frac{7}{17}$ **j)** $\frac{7}{21}$

4 **a)** $\frac{11}{12}$ **b)** $\frac{7}{18}$ **c)** $\frac{3}{23}$

   d) $\frac{16}{19}$ **e)** $\frac{9}{22}$ **f)** $\frac{13}{16}$

5 **a)** $\frac{2}{3}$ **b)** $\frac{1}{2}$ **c)** $\frac{4}{5}$ **d)** $\frac{2}{3}$ **e)** $\frac{2}{3}$

   f) $\frac{2}{3}$ **g)** $\frac{1}{3}$ **h)** $\frac{1}{2}$ **i)** $\frac{4}{5}$ **j)** $\frac{3}{4}$

6 $\frac{16}{21}$

7 $\frac{8}{35}$

8 $\frac{11}{18}$

9 $\frac{2}{9}$

Page 65   Exercise 2

1 a) $\frac{1}{6}+\frac{1}{3}=\frac{1}{6}+\frac{2}{6}=\frac{3}{6}$

b) $\frac{5}{9}+\frac{1}{3}=\frac{5}{9}+\frac{3}{9}=\frac{8}{9}$

c) $\frac{5}{6}-\frac{3}{12}=\frac{10}{12}-\frac{3}{12}=\frac{7}{12}$

d) $\frac{11}{12}-\frac{1}{3}=\frac{11}{12}-\frac{4}{12}=\frac{7}{12}$

2 a) $\frac{10}{15},\frac{3}{15}$ **b)** $\frac{13}{15}$

3 a) $\frac{12}{20},\frac{5}{20}$ **b)** $\frac{7}{20}$

4 a) $\frac{1}{2}$ **b)** $\frac{4}{5}$ **c)** $\frac{1}{3}$ **d)** $\frac{1}{4}$

e) $\frac{7}{24}$ **f)** $\frac{1}{10}$ **g)** $\frac{24}{25}$ **h)** $\frac{8}{11}$

5 a) $\frac{11}{12}$ **b)** $\frac{17}{24}$ **c)** $\frac{7}{10}$ **d)** $\frac{4}{15}$

e) $\frac{17}{21}$ **f)** $\frac{11}{20}$ **g)** $\frac{16}{35}$ **h)** $\frac{9}{28}$

6 $\frac{2}{3}$

7 $\frac{18}{35}$ m

8 $\frac{3}{8}$ kg

5.3 Multiplying and Dividing Fractions

Page 67   Exercise 1

1 a) 3   **b)** 4   **c)** 4
d) 7   **e)** 4   **f)** 4
g) 6   **h)** 5   **i)** 3

2 a) $12\times\frac{3}{4}=\frac{12\times3}{4}=\frac{36}{4}=9$

b) $20\times\frac{2}{5}=\frac{20\times2}{5}=\frac{40}{5}=8$

c) $9\times\frac{2}{9}=\frac{9\times2}{9}=\frac{18}{9}=2$

d) $6\times\frac{5}{6}=\frac{6\times5}{6}=\frac{30}{6}=5$

3 a) 4   **b)** 2   **c)** 6   **d)** 6   **e)** 2   **f)** 2
g) 4   **h)** 5   **i)** 3   **j)** 4   **k)** 6   **l)** 12

4 a) 4   **b)** 3   **c)** 9   **d)** 16   **e)** 9   **f)** 5
g) 8   **h)** 6   **i)** 15

5 12 sweets

6 20 cm

Page 69   Exercise 2

1 a) $\frac{1}{3}\times\frac{1}{4}=\frac{1\times1}{3\times4}=\frac{1}{12}$

b) $\frac{1}{3}\times\frac{1}{5}=\frac{1\times1}{3\times5}=\frac{1}{15}$

c) $\frac{3}{4}\times\frac{1}{7}=\frac{3\times1}{4\times7}=\frac{3}{28}$

d) $\frac{2}{5}\times\frac{3}{5}=\frac{2\times3}{5\times5}=\frac{6}{25}$

e) $\frac{5}{9}\times\frac{1}{4}=\frac{5\times1}{9\times4}=\frac{5}{36}$

f) $\frac{1}{9}\times\frac{1}{8}=\frac{1\times1}{9\times8}=\frac{1}{72}$

g) $\frac{1}{7}\times\frac{4}{5}=\frac{1\times4}{7\times5}=\frac{4}{35}$

h) $\frac{3}{7}\times\frac{4}{5}=\frac{3\times4}{7\times5}=\frac{12}{35}$

2 a) $\frac{5}{21}$ **b)** $\frac{1}{16}$ **c)** $\frac{2}{27}$ **d)** $\frac{3}{32}$ **e)** $\frac{3}{40}$

f) $\frac{1}{18}$ **g)** $\frac{4}{35}$ **h)** $\frac{4}{15}$ **i)** $\frac{1}{36}$ **j)** $\frac{2}{35}$

3 a) $\frac{8}{21}$ **b)** $\frac{12}{45}$ **c)** $\frac{30}{49}$ **d)** $\frac{25}{42}$

4 a) $\frac{3}{10}$ **b)** $\frac{1}{6}$ **c)** $\frac{1}{8}$ **d)** $\frac{4}{9}$ **e)** $\frac{1}{3}$

f) $\frac{1}{7}$ **g)** $\frac{1}{7}$ **h)** $\frac{2}{15}$ **i)** $\frac{1}{3}$ **j)** $\frac{2}{5}$

Page 71   Exercise 3

1 a) $\frac{6}{5}$ **b)** $\frac{3}{2}$ **c)** 9 or $\frac{9}{1}$ **d)** $\frac{9}{4}$

e) $\frac{10}{3}$ **f)** 6 or $\frac{6}{1}$ **g)** $\frac{7}{2}$ **h)** $\frac{11}{4}$

i) $\frac{5}{3}$ **j)** $\frac{8}{5}$ **k)** $\frac{4}{3}$ **l)** 10 or $\frac{10}{1}$

2 a) $\frac{1}{3}$ **b)** $\frac{1}{7}$ **c)** $\frac{1}{6}$ **d)** $\frac{1}{4}$

e) $\frac{1}{9}$ **f)** $\frac{1}{11}$ **g)** $\frac{1}{5}$ **h)** $\frac{1}{2}$

i) $\frac{1}{10}$ **j)** $\frac{1}{8}$ **k)** $\frac{1}{15}$ **l)** $\frac{1}{21}$

3 a) $\frac{1}{8}\div\frac{1}{4}=\frac{1}{8}\times\frac{4}{1}=\frac{1\times4}{8\times1}=\frac{4}{8}$

b) $\frac{2}{5}\div\frac{1}{2}=\frac{2}{5}\times\frac{2}{1}=\frac{2\times2}{5\times1}=\frac{4}{5}$

c) $\frac{1}{4}\div\frac{5}{6}=\frac{1}{4}\times\frac{6}{5}=\frac{1\times6}{4\times5}=\frac{6}{20}$

d) $\frac{4}{7}\div\frac{2}{3}=\frac{4}{7}\times\frac{3}{2}=\frac{4\times3}{7\times2}=\frac{12}{14}$

e) $\frac{3}{8}\div\frac{1}{2}=\frac{3}{8}\times\frac{2}{1}=\frac{3\times2}{8\times1}=\frac{6}{8}$

f) $\frac{1}{9}\div\frac{3}{8}=\frac{1}{9}\times\frac{8}{3}=\frac{1\times8}{9\times3}=\frac{8}{27}$

4 a) $\frac{8}{9}$ **b)** $\frac{4}{5}$ **c)** $\frac{5}{16}$

d) $\frac{36}{121}$ **e)** $\frac{2}{5}$ **f)** $\frac{2}{3}$

5 a) $3\div\frac{3}{5}=3\times\frac{5}{3}=\frac{3\times5}{3}=\frac{15}{3}=5$

b) $4\div\frac{2}{6}=4\times\frac{6}{2}=\frac{4\times6}{2}=\frac{24}{2}=12$

6 a) 33   **b)** 21   **c)** 6   **d)** 9   **e)** 20

7 a) $\frac{5}{6}\div4=\frac{5}{6}\times\frac{1}{4}=\frac{5\times1}{6\times4}=\frac{5}{24}$

b) $\frac{7}{8}\div6=\frac{7}{8}\times\frac{1}{6}=\frac{7\times1}{8\times6}=\frac{7}{48}$

8 a) $\frac{1}{6}$ **b)** $\frac{1}{3}$ **c)** $\frac{1}{6}$ **d)** $\frac{1}{16}$ **e)** $\frac{1}{33}$

9 $\frac{1}{7}$

10 $\frac{1}{10}$ m

11 $\frac{2}{9}$

5.4 Changing Fractions to Decimals and Percentages

Page 74   Exercise 1

1 a) 0.625　　　b) 0.15625　　c) 0.44
　d) 0.225　　　e) 0.5625　　　f) 0.0625
　g) 0.4375　　　h) 0.18　　　　i) 0.056
　j) 0.024　　　　k) 0.044　　　l) 0.1488
　m) 0.3125　　　n) 0.68　　　　o) 0.34375
　p) 0.144　　　　q) 0.804　　　r) 0.64

2 a) $\frac{9}{10}$ = 9 tenths = 0.9

　b) $\frac{5}{100}$ = 5 hundredths = 0.05

　c) $\frac{16}{1000}$ = 16 thousandths = 0.016

　d) $\frac{98}{100}$ = 98 hundredths = 0.98

　e) $\frac{83}{100}$ = 83 hundredths = 0.83

　f) $\frac{123}{1000}$ = 123 thousandths = 0.123

3 a) 0.4　　　b) 0.8　　　c) 0.2　　　d) 0.3
　e) 0.04　　　f) 0.06　　　g) 0.81　　h) 0.14
　i) 0.26　　　j) 0.002　　k) 0.005　　l) 0.057
　m) 0.039　　n) 0.391　　o) 0.998　　p) 0.017

4 a) 2　　　　　b) 0.2

5 a) $\frac{6}{10}$　　　　b) 0.6

6 a) i) $\frac{8}{10}$　　　ii) 0.8

　b) i) $\frac{2}{10}$　　　ii) 0.2

　c) i) $\frac{6}{10}$　　　ii) 0.6

　d) i) $\frac{9}{10}$　　　ii) 0.9

　e) i) $\frac{5}{10}$　　　ii) 0.5

　f) i) $\frac{3}{10}$　　　ii) 0.3

7 a) $\frac{22}{100}$　　　b) 0.22

Page 76   Exercise 2

1 a) 0.9 = 9 tenths = $\frac{9}{10}$

　b) 0.11 = 11 hundredths = $\frac{11}{100}$

　c) 0.03 = 3 hundredths = $\frac{3}{100}$

　d) 0.057 = 57 thousandths = $\frac{57}{1000}$

2 a) $\frac{3}{10}$　　　b) $\frac{7}{10}$　　　c) $\frac{1}{100}$
　d) $\frac{3}{1000}$　　e) $\frac{13}{100}$　　f) $\frac{17}{1000}$
　g) $\frac{47}{100}$　　h) $\frac{203}{1000}$　i) $\frac{63}{1000}$
　j) $\frac{9}{1000}$　　k) $\frac{81}{100}$　　l) $\frac{1}{100}$

3 a) $\frac{1}{2}$　　b) $\frac{4}{5}$　　c) $\frac{1}{5}$　　d) $\frac{3}{25}$
　e) $\frac{11}{25}$　　f) $\frac{19}{50}$　　g) $\frac{16}{25}$　　h) $\frac{1}{25}$
　i) $\frac{1}{20}$　　j) $\frac{9}{40}$　　k) $\frac{9}{200}$　　l) $\frac{1}{125}$

Page 77   Exercise 3

1 a) i) 53%　　ii) 47%　　b) i) 10%　　ii) 90%
　c) i) 13%　　ii) 87%　　d) i) 25%　　ii) 75%

2 a) 61%　　　b) 39%

3 a) 80%　　b) 40%　　c) 14%　　d) 36%
　e) 35%　　f) 8%　　　g) 61%　　h) 10%
　i) 65%　　j) 32%　　k) 60%　　l) 40%

4 72%

5 9%

6 82%

7 52%

Page 79   Exercise 4

1 a) 12%　　b) 37%　　c) 94%　　d) 61%
　e) 3%　　　f) 9%

2 a) i) 67%　　　ii) $\frac{67}{100}$

　b) i) 77%　　　ii) $\frac{77}{100}$

　c) i) 1%　　　ii) $\frac{1}{100}$

　d) i) 5%　　　ii) $\frac{1}{20}$

　e) i) 45%　　　ii) $\frac{9}{20}$

　f) i) 84%　　　ii) $\frac{21}{25}$

3 a) i) 0.49　　ii) 49%
　b) i) 0.33　　ii) 33%
　c) i) 0.3　　　ii) 30%
　d) i) 0.9　　　ii) 90%
　e) i) 0.5　　　ii) 50%
　f) i) 0.25　　ii) 25%
　g) i) 0.6　　　ii) 60%

4 a) i) 0.45　　ii) 45%
　b) i) 0.84　　ii) 84%
　c) i) 0.26　　ii) 26%
　d) i) 0.8　　　ii) 80%
　e) i) 0.45　　ii) 45%
　f) i) 0.4　　　ii) 40%

5 72%

6 0.4

7 10%

Page 80   Exercise 5

1 **a)** 0.12   **b)** 0.37   **c)** 0.8   **d)** 0.29
    e) 0.41   **f)** 0.03   **g)** 0.57   **h)** 0.92
    i) 0.45   **j)** 0.19   **k)** 0.06   **l)** 0.01

2 **a) i)** 0.39   **ii)** $\frac{39}{100}$

    b) i) 0.48   **ii)** $\frac{12}{25}$

    c) i) 0.5   **ii)** $\frac{1}{2}$

    d) i) 0.13   **ii)** $\frac{13}{100}$

    e) i) 0.09   **ii)** $\frac{9}{100}$

    f) i) 0.6   **ii)** $\frac{3}{5}$

    g) i) 0.25   **ii)** $\frac{1}{4}$

    h) i) 0.3   **ii)** $\frac{3}{10}$

    i) i) 0.55   **ii)** $\frac{11}{20}$

    j) i) 0.75   **ii)** $\frac{3}{4}$

    k) i) 0.05   **ii)** $\frac{1}{20}$

    l) i) 0.22   **ii)** $\frac{11}{50}$

3 0.64

4 $\frac{17}{20}$

5 0.47

6 $\frac{18}{25}$

Page 81   Exercise 6

1 **a)** 27%   **b)** $\frac{1}{2}$ **c)** 0.81   **d)** 0.66

2 **a)** $\frac{28}{100}$, 30%, 0.32   **b)** $\frac{1}{2}$, 0.56, 58%

    c) 19%, $\frac{1}{5}$, 0.22   **d)** $\frac{69}{100}$, 0.7, 71%

    e) $\frac{4}{10}$, 41%, 0.42   **f)** 0.04, 26%, $\frac{2}{5}$

3 **a)** 0.63   **b)** 0.6   **c)** $\frac{3}{5}$, 63%, 0.66

4 **a)** 0.44   **b)** 0.3   **c)** 0.65   **d)** 80%
    e) 0.3   **f)** 0.1   **g)** 0.8   **h)** $\frac{2}{20}$

5.5 Percentages of Amounts

Page 82   Exercise 1

1 **a)** 4   **b)** 3   **c)** 12 cm
    d) 5 kg   **e)** £3.50   **f)** 6 km

2 **a)** £5   **b)** £20

3 18

4 £300

5 6000

6 40

7 24

8 **a)** 6   **b)** 12

9 **a)** 9   **b)** 27

10 **a)** 7 kg   **b)** 28 kg

11 **a)** £3   **b)** £18

12 **a)** £24   **b)** 24p   **c)** 12 cm   **d)** 35 miles

13 **a)** 4   **b)** 2

14 **a)** 16 km   **b)** 8 km

15 **a)** 6   **b)** 3   **c)** 9

16 **a)** £30   **b)** £15   **c)** £105

17 £36

18 £0.90 (or 90p)

Page 84   Exercise 2

1 **a)** $\frac{24}{100}$ × 25 ⟶ 24 ÷ 100 × 25 = 6

    b) $\frac{65}{100}$ × 180 ⟶ 65 ÷ 100 × 180 = 117

    c) $\frac{17}{100}$ × 40 ⟶ 17 ÷ 100 × 40 = 6.8

2 **a)** 56   **b)** 216   **c)** 186
    d) 224   **e)** 165   **f)** 9
    g) 345   **h)** 179.4   **i)** 46.4
    j) 316.2   **k)** 20.16   **l)** 41.4

3 **a)** £11.25   **b)** £7.20   **c)** £7.35
    d) £48.30   **e)** £14.16   **f)** £10.50

4 462

5 £38.72

6 63 g

7 £3.38

8 51

9 119 miles

10 **a)** 124   **b)** 140   **c)** 144

5.6 Percentage Change

Page 86   Exercise 1

1 **a)** 15   **b)** 45   **c)** 99
    d) 60   **e)** £44   **f)** 18
    g) £60   **h)** 63   **i)** £45

2 **a)** 240   **b)** 210   **c)** 117 kg
    d) 490   **e)** 320   **f)** 140
    g) 152 cm   **h)** £192   **i)** 92 g

3 **a)** £46   **b)** 2.5 cm   **c)** £67.50
    d) 8 m   **e)** 35 mm   **f)** 78 cm
    g) £7.50   **h)** 496 kg   **i)** £3.85
    j) 435 km

4 **a)** 155 kg   **b)** 114 miles   **c)** £427
    d) £236   **e)** 168 km   **f)** $288
    g) 53.5 cm   **h)** 211.2 kg   **i)** £616.25
    j) 2576 g

5 **a)** 288 kg   **b)** 135 m   **c)** £288
    d) £329   **e)** £194.30   **f)** £173.90
    g) 104 mm   **h)** £312   **i)** £22.40
    j) 1104 miles

6 250 g

7 £88

8 £280

9 £36

10 1080 visitors
11 £52.50
12 £1.08 (or 108p)
13 £852.80
14 £32.25
15 £4.35

Section 6 — Ratio and Proportion

6.1 Comparing Quantities

Page 89   Exercise 1

1 a) $\frac{4}{5}$ b) $\frac{5}{8}$ c) $\frac{1}{3}$ d) $\frac{1}{2}$

2 a) $\frac{3}{2}$ b) $\frac{9}{4}$ c) $\frac{7}{4}$ d) $\frac{19}{12}$

3 a) i) $\frac{11}{16}$ ii) $\frac{16}{11}$

   b) $\frac{11}{16}$

4 a) i) $\frac{5}{6}$ ii) $\frac{6}{5}$

   b) $\frac{6}{5}$

5 a) $\frac{4}{5}$ b) $\frac{7}{6}$

6 $\frac{4}{3}$

7 $\frac{5}{3}$

8 a) $\frac{1}{3}$ b) $\frac{7}{4}$ c) green, pink

Page 91   Exercise 2

1 a) 70%   b) 30%   c) 75%   d) 60%
2 a) 120%   b) 115%   c) 200%   d) 250%
3 a) 80%   b) 125%
4 a) 40%   b) 250%
5 a) 65%   b) 180%   c) 520%

Page 92   Exercise 3

1 a) £3   b) 20%
2 a) £4   b) 40%
3 a) £1.50   b) 25%
4 a) £120   b) 30%
5 50%
6 60%
7 20%
8 300%

Page 93   Exercise 4

1 a) 2:5   b) 5:2
2 a) 1:4   b) 4:1
3 a) 15:19   b) 19:15
4 7:5
5 a) 37:81   b) 81:37
6 10:3
7 2:7

8 78:61
9 9:8
10 a) 2:1   b) 1:4   c) 1:2   d) 1:5
11 a) 3:1   b) 1:3
12 a) 13:11   b) 11:2   c) 13:11:2
13 a) $\frac{2}{5}$ b) $\frac{5}{2}$ c) $\frac{5}{7}$
14 a) 6:1   b) $\frac{1}{6}$
15 a) $\frac{1}{5}$ b) 4:1   c) $\frac{1}{4}$
16 4:1:2
17 a) $\frac{3}{4}$ b) 300%   c) $\frac{1}{2}$

6.2 Ratio and Proportion

Page 97   Exercise 1

1 a) 1:2   b) 1:2   c) 1:3   d) 1:4
   e) 4:1   f) 2:1   g) 3:1   h) 2:1
   i) 2:3   j) 3:5   k) 2:5   l) 2:5
   m) 5:4   n) 3:2   o) 3:2   p) 3:2
2 2:1
3 1:3
4 a) 5:9   b) 3:7
5 2:3
6 5:2

Page 98   Exercise 2

1 8
2 27
3 15
4 12
5 6 litres
6 200 g
7 £9
8 105 cm
9 2.2 m

Page 100   Exercise 3

1 a) 4 and 12   b) 9 and 12
2 a) 9 and 24   b) 18 and 21
3 a) £5 and £25   b) £12 and £18
   c) £9 and £21   d) £14 and £16
4 a) 16 kg and 48 kg   b) 8 kg and 56 kg
   c) 20 kg and 44 kg   d) 30 kg and 34 kg
5 a) 78 ml   b) 42 mm   c) £78   d) 340 g
6 335
7 Justin — £560, Lee — £1440

Section 7 — Units and Scales

7.1 Time

Page 101   Exercise 1

1 a) 07:35   b) 12:15   c) 03:20   d) 14:40
   e) 11:50   f) 22:25   g) 00:11   h) 17:48

2 a) 9:50 am   b) 3:20 pm   c) 4:15 am   d) 12:18 pm
   e) 11:25 am   f) 7:40 pm   g) 12:45 am   h) 10:42 pm

3 a) i) 4:00 pm   ii) 16:00
   b) i) 8:30 am   ii) 08:30
   c) i) 11:10 pm   ii) 23:10
   d) i) 6:15 am   ii) 06:15
   e) i) 2:45 pm   ii) 14:45
   f) i) 6:35 pm   ii) 18:35

Page 102   Exercise 2

1 a) 120 minutes   b) 360 minutes
   c) 270 minutes   d) 325 minutes

2 a) 300 seconds   b) 480 seconds   c) 900 seconds
   d) 660 seconds   e) 195 seconds   f) 250 seconds

3 a) 3 hours   b) 2 hours 30 minutes
   c) 3 hours 45 minutes   d) 4 hours 7 minutes

4 a) 5 minutes   b) 1 minute 30 seconds
   c) 2 minutes 16 seconds d) 3 minutes 19 seconds

5 a) 5.5 hours   b) 1.75 hours   c) 3.2 hours

6 a) 30 minutes   b) 210 minutes

7 195 seconds

8 a) 90 minutes   b) 5400 seconds

Page 104   Exercise 3

1 65 minutes (or 1 hour and 5 minutes)

2 a) 9:10 am   b) 2:10 pm
   c) 18:01   d) 17:08

3 08:44

4 12:10

5 6:35 pm

6 a) 45 minutes   b) 35 minutes
   c) 1 hour and 25 minutes or 85 minutes
   d) 3 hours and 50 minutes or 230 minutes

7 2 hours and 20 minutes or 140 minutes

8 4 hours and 20 minutes or 260 minutes

9 10:58 am

10 18:05

Page 106   Exercise 4

1 a) 06:32   b) 08:06
   c) 1 hour and 34 minutes

2 a) 11:36   b) 13:43   c) 11:36 am and 1:43 pm

3 a) 07:47   b) 1 hour and 2 minutes   c) 08:02

4 09:58

5 a) 07:47   b) Yes

Page 107   Exercise 5

1 a) 5 km/h   b) 4 km/h   c) 5 km/h
   d) 30 km/h   e) 20 km/h   f) 500 km/h

2 60 mph

3 5 m/s

4 500 mph

5 a) 8 km/h   b) 35 mph   c) 6.25 m/s
   d) 9.6 km/h   e) 5 m/s   f) 0.025 m/s

6 a) 0.5 hours   b) 36 km/h

7 a) 0.25 hours   b) 17 000 mph

8 a) 70 mph   b) 36 km/h   c) 5.5 km/h
   d) 800 km/h   e) 5 km/h   f) 17 mph

7.2 Money

Page 110   Exercise 1

1 a) £44.50   b) £43.65
   c) £24.20   d) £69.66

2 €510

3 a) One £5 note and one £2 coin
   b) One £10 note, one £5 note and one £1 coin
   c) One £20 note, one £5 note, one £2 coin
      and one £1 coin
   d) One £10 note, one £2 coin, one 50p coin
   e) One £20 note, one £1 coin, one 20p coin and
      one 10p coin
   f) One £20 note, one £10 note, one £2 coin,
      one 20p coin and one 5p coin
   g) One £2 coin, one 10p coin, one 5p coin, one 2p coin
      and one 1p coin
   h) One £10 note, one £1 coin, one 50p coin,
      one 20p coin, one 10p coin and two 2p coins

4 a) £6.60
   b) One £5 note, one £1 coin, one 50p coin
      and one 10p coin

5 a) $15   b) $300   c) $180   d) $120
   e) $112.50   f) $247.50   g) $442.50   h) $48.75

6 a) €24   b) €600   c) €420   d) €72
   e) €54   f) €234   g) €282   h) €27

7 a) €57.50   b) €207   c) €1725   d) €833.75

8 £40

9 £500

10 £500

Page 111   Exercise 2

1 a) £24   b) £56   c) £120

2 a) £1.50   b) £30

3 a) £0.90 or 90p   b) £7.20   c) £22.50

4 a) £15   b) £4.50   c) £150

5 £66

6 £6.50

7 a) £0.65 or 65p   b) £0.60 or 60p   c) the large box

8 a) 1.5p   b) 1.6p   c) the small bottle

9 The bag of 12 apples

10 The 500 g bag of cotton wool

11 1.5 m of ribbon

12 1 hour

13 a) 5 biscuits   b) 11 biscuits

14 6.25 kg

15 153 miles

16 32 cars

7.3 Units and Measuring

Page 114 Exercise 1

1 a) 16 cm   b) 24 cm   c) 11 cm

2 a) 25 cm   b) 5 cm   c) 45 cm

3 a) A = 4 cm, B = 7 cm, C = 8.5 cm
   b) A = 40 mm, B = 65 mm, C = 90 mm
   c) A = 8.2 cm, B = 8.4 cm, C = 8.7 cm

4 a) 300 ml   b) 3.5 litres   c) 5 cm³
   d) 16 cm³   e) 2.25 litres   f) 2.2 ml

5 a) 25 kg   b) 350 g   c) 7.5 tonnes
   d) 10 tonnes   e) 250 g   f) 1.75 kg

Page 117 Exercise 2

1 a) 60 mm   b) 3000 kg
   c) 4000 ml   d) 900 cm
   e) 12 000 g   f) 15 000 m
   g) 120 cm³   h) 140 mm

2 a) 5700 g   b) 25 mm
   c) 1600 m   d) 1120 cm
   e) 8300 ml   f) 4900 g
   g) 3.6 cm³   h) 800 kg

3 a) 7 m   b) 50 ml
   c) 12 cm   d) 2 tonnes
   e) 6 litres   f) 10 km
   g) 14 m   h) 19 litres

4 a) 5.8 cm   b) 4.5 kg
   c) 3.2 litres   d) 5.8 m
   e) 11.4 tonnes   f) 7.8 km
   g) 96.5 cm   h) 0.9 kg

5 a) 2.8 cm   b) 4.7 kg
   c) 0.6 litres   d) 2.4 km
   e) 170 cm   f) 30 500 ml
   g) 27.8 cm³   h) 117 mm

6 130 mm

7 1200 g

8 0.4 litres

9 6.8 tonnes

10 1.6 km

11 1.4 kg

12 a) 1240 mm   b) 1.24 m

13 a) 3500 ml   b) 20 tea cups

14 a) 300 kg   b) 300 000 g

Page 119 Exercise 3

1 a) i) 3   ii) divide
   b) i) 16   ii) multiply
   c) i) 8   ii) divide
   d) i) 12   ii) multiply
   e) i) 14   ii) divide
   f) i) 12   ii) divide

2 a) 48 inches   b) 42 pounds   c) 40 pints
   d) 32 ounces   e) 36 feet   f) 7 pounds

3 a) 3 feet   b) 10 gallons   c) 2 stone
   d) 7 yards   e) 2.5 pounds   f) 3.75 gallons

4 a) 9 yards   b) 56 ounces
   c) 15 gallons   d) 10 pounds

5 a) 1 foot 6 inches   b) 7 stone 6 pounds

6 4 feet 8 inches

7 80 glasses

7.4 Maps and Scale Drawings

Page 121 Exercise 1

1 a) i) 8 km   ii) 10 km   iii) 16 km
     iv) 20 km   v) 25 km   vi) 33 km
   b) i) 3 cm   ii) 7 cm   iii) 12 cm
     iv) 20 cm   v) 50 cm   vi) 17.5 cm

2 5 cm

3 a) 100 km   b) 140 km   c) 220 km
   d) 130 km   e) 250 km   f) 295 km

4 a) 3 cm   b) 8 cm   c) 10 cm
   d) 4.5 cm   e) 9.5 cm   f) 2.8 cm

5 550 km

6 a) 10 m   b) 25 m   c) 40 m
   d) 17.5 m   e) 32.5 m   f) 21 m

7 a) 2 cm   b) 4 cm   c) 5 cm
   d) 2.5 cm   e) 4.5 cm   f) 6.25 cm

8 14.4 cm

9 a) 3 cm   b) 1 km   c) 0.5 cm by 1 cm

10 a) 10 cm   b) 20 cm   c) 5 cm   d) 3 cm

Page 123 Exercise 2

1 6 cm

2 5000 cm

3 a) i) 20 m   ii) 50 m   iii) 60 m
     iv) 75 m   v) 32.5 m   vi) 72.5 m
   b) i) 1 cm   ii) 2 cm   iii) 8 cm
     iv) 2.5 cm   v) 1.5 cm   vi) 1.7 cm

4 a) 10 m   b) 17.5 m   c) 30 m
   d) 26.25 m   e) 46.25 m   f) 16.5 m

5 a) 2 cm   b) 4.5 cm   c) 11 cm
   d) 1 cm   e) 1.5 cm   f) 6 cm

6 a) 800 000 cm   b) 8000 m   c) 8 km

Page 126 Exercise 3

1 a) a = 1 m, b = 1.5 m, c = 2 m
   b) a = 2.5 m, b = 1 m, c = 1.5 m

2 a) Scale drawing should have measurements:

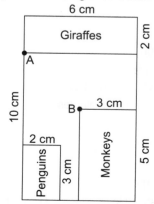

   b) 21 m

3 a) 2 m by 3 m   **b)** 2 m by 1 m

c) E.g. Scale drawing should have measurements:

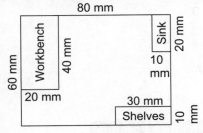

4 Scale drawing should have measurements:

Section 8 — Algebraic Expressions

8.1 Expressions

Page 128   Exercise 1

1 a) 3   **b)** 2   **c)** 3   **d)** 3
e) 1   **f)** 2   **g)** 3   **h)** 2
i) 2   **j)** 2   **k)** 2   **l)** 3

2 a) $+m, +9, +n$ **b)** $+a, -bc, +d^2$
c) $+11r, -2, +t$ **d)** $-p, -q, +7$
e) $+ab, +cd$ **f)** $+y, +7, -yz$
g) $+xyz$ **h)** $+q, -rs, +4, +t$
i) $+f^2, +g^2h$ **j)** $-v^2, -v, +2$
k) $+8, -c^3, -c^2$ **l)** $+1, -xyz, +z^3, -y$

3 a) y^3 **b)** n^3 **c)** q^4 **d)** a^2
e) ab^2 **f)** $6m^2$ **g)** $16r^2$ **h)** $15x^2$
i) $18y^2$ **j)** $24d^2$ **k)** $21st$ **l)** $132ik$

8.2 Simplifying Expressions

Page 129   Exercise 1

1 a) $9y$ **b)** $6b$ **c)** $3d$ **d)** $13t$ **e)** $5x$
f) $9y$ **g)** $10p$ **h)** s **i)** $5w$ **j)** $15n$

2 a) $9d$ **b)** $7x$ **c)** $15w$
d) y **e)** $6t$ **f)** $5n$
g) $15s$ **h)** $3z$ **i)** $5g$
j) $2a$ **k)** $6x$ **l)** $2w$
m) r **n)** $3h$ **o)** $11n$

3 a) $3x + 4y$ **b)** $3a + 8b$ **c)** $6m + 5n$
d) $3p + q$ **e)** $9f - 7g$ **f)** $2a + 6c$
g) $x - 6y$ **h)** $6p - 5q$ **i)** $4f + 4g$
j) $8s + 2t$ **k)** $6x + y$ **l)** $15m + 3n$
m) $4d - 5e$ **n)** $8p - 14q$ **o)** $-12i - 3j$

4 a) $12f + 13$ **b)** $17x + 12$ **c)** $3y - 5$
d) $3s - 6$ **e)** $7f + 10$ **f)** $5a + 11$
g) $5x + 7$ **h)** $9q - 1$ **i)** $5g - 7$
j) $y + 7$ **k)** $4s + 22$ **l)** $2h - 15$

5 a) $11y - 3x$ **b)** $14c + 7d$ **c)** $16r + 6s$
d) $-3g - 3j$ **e)** $16w - 16u$ **f)** $3y - 4z$
g) $v - 13w$ **h)** $13g - 6h$

8.3 Expressions with Brackets

Page 131   Exercise 1

1 a) $3c + 6$ **b)** $4d + 24$ **c)** $2r + 14$
d) $20 + 5x$ **e)** $9g - 9$ **f)** $11f - 88$
g) $36 + 12m$ **h)** $7 - 7e$ **i)** $48 + 6c$

2 a) $de + 2d$ **b)** $xy - 7x$ **c)** $wh - 4w$
d) $6s + st$ **e)** $3m + mp$ **f)** $8x - xy$
g) $g^2 + 10g$ **h)** $p^2 + 3p$ **i)** $s^2 - 9s$
j) $11m + m^2$ **k)** $6y + y^2$ **l)** $12z + z^2$

3 a) $12n + 32$ **b)** $12p - 6$ **c)** $54q + 6$
d) $63x + 45$ **e)** $12y - 6$ **f)** $24 + 16w$
g) $132 + 24c$ **h)** $63 - 42d$ **i)** $20 - 20g$

4 a) $10a^2 - 18a$ **b)** $12d^2 + 28d$ **c)** $60g^2 - 25g$
d) $6n^2 + 24n$ **e)** $33x + 6x^2$ **f)** $12y - 24y^2$
g) $48t^2 - 132t$ **h)** $20w^2 + 90w$ **i)** $63p + 42p^2$

5 a) $8v - 4x$ **b)** $2b - 12c$ **c)** $8g + 40h$
d) $44f + 11n$ **e)** $12p^2 + 16ps$ **f)** $6t^2 + 24nt$
g) $16uk - 6u^2$ **h)** $5hr + 35h^2$ **i)** $54v^2 + 30vm$

Page 133   Exercise 2

1 a) 9   **b)** a, 3   **c)** $9(a + 3)$
2 a) 4   **b)** $3b$, 4   **c)** $4(3b - 4)$
3 a) 3   **b)** $3(5 - 8x)$
4 a) $9(1 + 2a)$ **b)** $4(3 + b)$ **c)** $5(1 - 5c)$
d) $4(2x + 5)$ **e)** $3(2d + 11)$ **f)** $12(x + 5)$
g) $7(2y + 7)$ **h)** $5(7 + 3v)$ **i)** $4(2c - 13)$
j) $4(4p - 3)$ **k)** $11(10 - 3x)$ **l)** $6(3x + 11)$

Section 9 — Equations

9.1 Solving Equations

Page 134   Exercise 1

1 a) $x = 5$ **b)** $x = 22$ **c)** $x = 59$ **d)** $x = 33$
e) $x = 87$ **f)** $x = 29$ **g)** $x = 5$ **h)** $x = 13$
i) $x = 48$ **j)** $x = 39$ **k)** $x = 20$ **l)** $x = 26$
m) $x = 31$ **n)** $x = 5$ **o)** $x = 56$ **p)** $x = 14$

2 a) $x = 3$ **b)** $x = 13$ **c)** $x = 5$ **d)** $x = 12$
e) $x = 7$ **f)** $x = 3$ **g)** $x = 10$ **h)** $x = 4$
i) $x = 15$ **j)** $x = 21$ **k)** $x = 24$ **l)** $x = 6$
m) $x = 10$ **n)** $x = 8$ **o)** $x = 6$ **p)** $x = 4$
q) $x = 2$ **r)** $x = 14$ **s)** $x = 8$ **t)** $x = 29$

3 a) $p = 5$ **b)** $b = 7$ **c)** $y = 3$ **d)** $x = 17$
e) $t = 15$ **f)** $s = 15$ **g)** $n = 22$ **h)** $z = 19$
i) $n = 13$ **j)** $y = 11$ **k)** $x = 10$ **l)** $t = 13$
m) $m = 16$ **n)** $p = 27$ **o)** $r = 12$ **p)** $y = 21$
q) $t = 1$ **r)** $y = 37$ **s)** $x = 23$ **t)** $s = 88$

Page 135   Exercise 2

1 **a)** $x = 3$ **b)** $x = 12$ **c)** $x = 6$
   d) $x = 7$ **e)** $x = 6$ **f)** $x = 11$
   g) $x = 8$ **h)** $x = 9$ **i)** $x = 12$
   j) $x = 28$ **k)** $x = 13$ **l)** $x = 21$

2 **a)** $y = 3$ **b)** $y = 5$ **c)** $y = 6$
   d) $y = 5$ **e)** $y = 8$ **f)** $y = 7$
   g) $y = 9$ **h)** $y = 10$ **i)** $y = 8$
   j) $y = 12$ **k)** $y = 4$ **l)** $y = 13$
   m) $y = 18$ **n)** $y = 14$ **o)** $y = 18$

3 **a)** $m = 4.5$ **b)** $n = 1.25$ **c)** $a = 2.5$
   d) $x = 1.5$ **e)** $y = 2.5$ **f)** $x = 3.2$
   g) $y = 2.6$ **h)** $t = 3.75$ **i)** $z = 4.25$
   j) $p = 2.25$ **k)** $r = 3.5$ **l)** $p = 2.25$

4 **a)** $p = 1.5$ **b)** $b = 1.25$ **c)** $z = 2.2$
   d) $s = 4.5$ **e)** $r = 3.5$ **f)** $n = 1.75$
   g) $a = 2.75$ **h)** $y = 4.5$ **i)** $x = 2.8$
   j) $y = 2.6$ **k)** $t = 4.25$ **l)** $x = 3.75$

Page 137   Exercise 3

1 **a)** $x = 8$ **b)** $x = 7$ **c)** $x = 6$
   d) $x = 6$ **e)** $x = 30$ **f)** $x = 6$
   g) $x = 4$ **h)** $x = 4$ **i)** $x = 12$

2 **a)** $p = 10$ **b)** $s = 6$ **c)** $t = 8$
   d) $r = 8$ **e)** $m = 3$ **f)** $n = 6$
   g) $y = 8$ **h)** $x = 7$ **i)** $z = 12$

3 **a)** $x = 11$ **b)** $x = 3$ **c)** $x = 10$
   d) $x = 7$ **e)** $x = 6$ **f)** $x = 6$
   g) $x = 6$ **h)** $x = 3$ **i)** $x = 5$
   j) $x = 7$ **k)** $x = 4$ **l)** $x = 3$

Section 10 — Formulas

10.1 Writing Formulas

Page 138   Exercise 1

1 **a)** $a = b + 2$ **b)** $a = b + 100$
   c) $a = b - 4$ **d)** $a = b - 2.5$
   e) $a = 7b$ **f)** $a = 10b$
   g) $a = \frac{1}{2}b$ or $a = \frac{b}{2}$ **h)** $a = b$
   i) $a = \frac{1}{3}b$ or $a = \frac{b}{3}$ **j)** $a = 2b$

2 **a)** a is five less than b
   b) x is six less than y
   c) T is fourteen more than Q
   d) g is nine more than h
   e) l is three times as big as m
   f) c is one hundred times as big as e
   g) q is the same as r
   h) j is a quarter of k
   i) p is two thirds of h
   j) z is four times as big as y
   k) t is fourteen times as big as v

3 $m = n - 2$

4 $s = r + 5$

5 $u = t - 10$

6 $y = x - 1$

7 $p = n + 4.5$

8 $b = 5a$

9 $c = 8s$

10 $w = 2q$

11 $h = \frac{1}{2}m$ or $h = \frac{m}{2}$

12 $y = \frac{1}{3}x$ or $y = \frac{x}{3}$

13 $c = \frac{1}{4}d$ or $c = \frac{d}{4}$

14 $f = \frac{1}{7}c$ or $f = \frac{c}{7}$

15 $r = 5 - s$

16 **a)** $j = k - 3$ **b)** $k = j + 3$

10.2 Substituting into a Formula

Page 141   Exercise 1

1 **a)** 5   **b)** 1
2 **a)** 12   **b)** 2
3 **a)** 6   **b)** 4   **c)** 1   **d)** 3
4 **a)** 11   **b)** 4   **c)** 14   **d)** 2
5 **a)** 15   **b)** 35   **c)** 100   **d)** 500
6 **a)** 2   **b)** 4   **c)** 5   **d)** 10

Page 142   Exercise 2

1 **a)** 5   **b)** 32   **c)** 1   **d)** 15
2 **a)** 2   **b)** 6   **c)** 5   **d)** 18
3 **a)** £18   **b)** £20   **c)** £25   **d)** £115
4 **a)** 215p or £2.15   **b)** 115p or £1.15
   c) 255p or £2.55   **d)** 135p or £1.35
5 £14

Page 143   Exercise 3

1 28 cm
2 99 m²
3 90 miles
4 35 cm²
5 **a)** 30   **b)** 56   **c)** 108   **d)** 9
   e) 12.5   **f)** 5.25

Section 11 — Sequences

11.1 Term-to-Term Rules

Page 144   Exercise 1

1 **a)** 1, 3, 5, 7, 9
   b) Add 2 each time

2 Add 2 each time

3 **a)** Add 4 each time   **b)** Add 3 each time
   c) Add 2 each time   **d)** Add 7 each time
   e) Add 10 each time   **f)** Add 8 each time
   g) Add 12 each time   **h)** Add 9 each time

4 **a)** Subtract 3 each time   **b)** Subtract 2 each time
c) Subtract 4 each time   **d)** Subtract 5 each time
e) Subtract 6 each time   **f)** Subtract 5 each time
g) Subtract 11 each time   **h)** Subtract 8 each time

5 **a)** Subtract 6 each time   **b)** Add 6 each time
c) Add 11 each time   **d)** Add 15 each time
e) Add 14 each time   **f)** Subtract 18 each time
g) Subtract 5 each time   **h)** Subtract 24 each time

6 **a)** Multiply by 4 each time   **b)** Multiply by 5 each time
c) Multiply by 3 each time   **d)** Multiply by 2 each time
e) Multiply by 4 each time   **f)** Multiply by 5 each time
g) Multiply by 3 each time   **h)** Multiply by 7 each time

7 **a)** Divide by 2 each time   **b)** Divide by 3 each time
c) Divide by 2 each time   **d)** Divide by 4 each time
e) Divide by 3 each time   **f)** Divide by 4 each time
g) Divide by 4 each time   **h)** Divide by 6 each time

8 **a)** Add 7 each time   **b)** Subtract 13 each time
c) Divide by 10 each time   **d)** Add 32 each time
e) Multiply by 9 each time   **f)** Subtract 18 each time
g) Divide by 5 each time   **h)** Add 5 each time
i) Multiply by 5 each time   **j)** Add 12 each time
k) Divide by 4 each time   **l)** Add 5 each time
m) Divide by 2 each time   **n)** Multiply by 10 each time

Page 146   **Exercise 2**

1 **a)** 7, 9, 11, 13, 15   **b)** 18, 14, 10, 6, 2
c) 3, 12, 48, 192, 768   **d)** 4375, 875, 175, 35, 7
2 **a)** 17, 41, 65, 89, 113, 137   **b)** 88, 75, 62, 49, 36, 23
c) 6, 24, 96, 384, 1536, 6144
d) 4000, 400, 40, 4, 0.4, 0.04
3 **a)** 42, 48, 54, 60, 66
b) 27, 33, 39, 45, 51
c) 0.5, 6.5, 12.5, 18.5, 24.5
4 **a)** 52, 40, 28, 16, 4
b) 89, 77, 65, 53, 41
c) 61, 49, 37, 25, 13
5 **a)** 8, 56, 392, 2744, 19 208
b) 14, 98, 686, 4802, 33 614
c) 21, 147, 1029, 7203, 50 421
6 **a)** 768, 192, 48, 12, 3
b) 1792, 448, 112, 28, 7
c) 3328, 832, 208, 52, 13
7 **a) i)** Add 9 each time   **ii)** 30, 39
b) i) Add 6 each time   **ii)** 26, 32
c) i) Subtract 6 each time   **ii)** 11, 5
d) i) Subtract 4 each time   **ii)** 25, 21
e) i) Add 13 each time   **ii)** 80, 93
f) i) Subtract 15 each time   **ii)** 37, 22
g) i) Add 14 each time   **ii)** 54, 68
h) i) Subtract 50 each time   **ii)** 550, 500
8 **a) i)** Multiply by 7 each time   **ii)** 686, 4802
b) i) Multiply by 10 each time   **ii)** 6000, 60 000
c) i) Multiply by 2 each time   **ii)** 96, 192
d) i) Divide by 10 each time   **ii)** 30, 3

Page 149   **Exercise 3**

1 **a) i)** 3, 4, 5   **ii)** Add 1 dot each time
iii)
b) i) 1, 4, 7   **ii)** Add 3 dots each time
iii)

2 **a)**
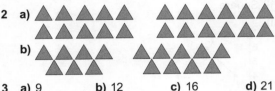
b)

3 **a)** 9   **b)** 12   **c)** 16   **d)** 21
4 **a)** 19, 25   **b)** 7, 9

11.2 Position-to-Term Rules

Page 150   **Exercise 1**
1 **a) i)** 4, 8, 12   **ii)** Multiply the position by 4   **iii)** 40
b) i) 5, 10, 15   **ii)** Multiply the position by 5   **iii)** 50
2 **a) i)** 20   **ii)** 200
b) i) 80   **ii)** 800
c) i) 30   **ii)** 300
d) i) 60   **ii)** 600
3 **a)** 200   **b)** 900   **c)** 1200   **d)** 1100
e) 700   **f)** 1300   **g)** 600   **h)** 1500
i) 10 000   **j)** −100

Section 12 — Graphs and Equations

12.1 Coordinates

Page 152   **Exercise 1**
1 **a)** 3   **b)** 2   **c)** 6
2 **a)** 6   **b)** 3   **c)** 0
3 $A(5, 2)$, $B(1, 8)$, $C(9, 5)$
4 **a) i)**

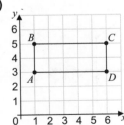

ii) Rectangle
b) i)

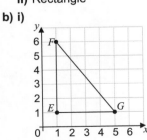

ii) Triangle

c) i)

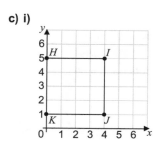

ii) Square

d) i)

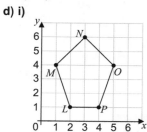

ii) Pentagon

Page 154 Exercise 2

1 **a)** $A = 5$, $B = -4$, $C = 4$, $D = -2$

   b) $A = 3$, $B = 2$, $C = -2$, $D = -3$

2 $A\ (-3, -4)$ $B\ (-2, -3)$ $C\ (2, -1)$
   $D\ (0, 1)$ $E\ (4, -3)$ $F\ (-2, 1)$
   $G\ (3, 2)$ $H\ (-4, 2)$

3 **a)** SQUARE   **b)** CIRCLE   **c)** CUBOID

4

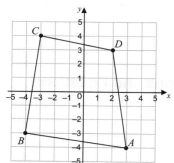

5 **a)**

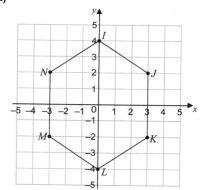

   b) Hexagon

12.2 Plotting Graphs

Page 156 Exercise 1

1 **a)**

x	0	1	2	3	4	5
y	4	5	6	7	8	9
Coords	(0, 4)	(1, 5)	(2, 6)	(3, 7)	(4, 8)	(5, 9)

b) and c)

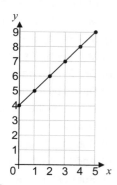

2 **a)**

x	0	1	2	3	4	5
y	0	2	4	6	8	10
Coords	(0, 0)	(1, 2)	(2, 4)	(3, 6)	(4, 8)	(5, 10)

b) and c)

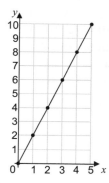

3 **a)**

x	1	2	3	4	5
y	0	1	2	3	4
Coords	(1, 0)	(2, 1)	(3, 2)	(4, 3)	(5, 4)

b) and c)

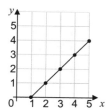

4 **a)**

x	0	1	2	3	4	5
y	5	4	3	2	1	0
Coords	(0, 5)	(1, 4)	(2, 3)	(3, 2)	(4, 1)	(5, 0)

b) and c)

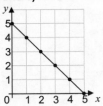

c) i)

x	−1	0	1	2
y	1	2	3	4
Coords	(−1, 1)	(0, 2)	(1, 3)	(2, 4)

ii)

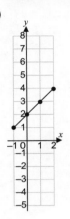

5 a)

x	0	1	2	3	4	5
y	0	−1	−2	−3	−4	−5
Coords	(0, 0)	(1, −1)	(2, −2)	(3, −3)	(4, −4)	(5, −5)

b) and c)

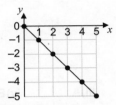

d) i)

x	−1	0	1	2
y	−5	−4	−3	−2
Coords	(−1, −5)	(0, −4)	(1, −3)	(2, −2)

ii)

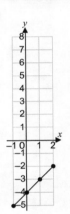

6 a) i)

x	−1	0	1	2
y	5	6	7	8
Coords	(−1, 5)	(0, 6)	(1, 7)	(2, 8)

ii)

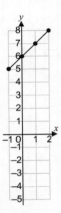

b) i)

x	−1	0	1	2
y	−3	−2	−1	0
Coords	(−1, −3)	(0, −2)	(1, −1)	(2, 0)

ii)

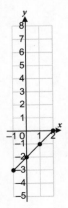

e) i)

x	−1	0	1	2
y	−4	−3	−2	−1
Coords	(−1, −4)	(0, −3)	(1, −2)	(2, −1)

ii)

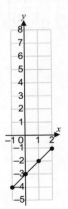

f) i)

x	−1	0	1	2
y	−1	0	1	2
Coords	(−1, −1)	(0, 0)	(1, 1)	(2, 2)

ii)

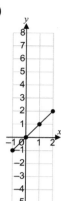

7 a)

x	0	1	2	3	4
y	0	3	6	9	12
Coords	(0, 0)	(1, 3)	(2, 6)	(3, 9)	(4, 12)

b) and c)

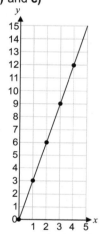

8 a)

x	0	1	2	3
$3x$	0	3	6	9
$3x + 2$	2	5	8	11
Coords	(0, 2)	(1, 5)	(2, 8)	(3, 11)

b) and c)

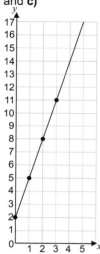

12.3 Interpreting Graphs

Page 159   Exercise 1

1 a) i) B   **ii)** C   **iii)** A   **iv)** E

   b) $y = -2$

   c) i) $y = 0$ **ii)** $x = 0$

2 a)

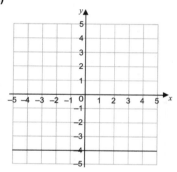

   b) $y = -4$

3 a)

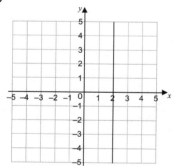

   b) $x = 2$

4 a)-f)

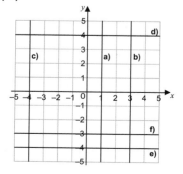

5 $y = 7$

6 $x = -3$

7 $x = 2$

8 $y = 4$

9 a) i) E.g.

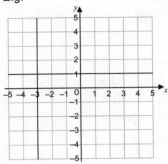

ii) E.g.

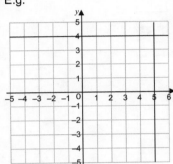

iii) E.g.

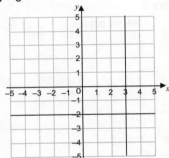

iv) E.g.

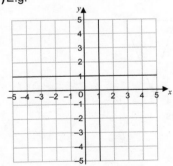

v) E.g.

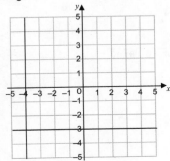

vi) E.g.

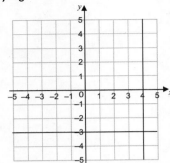

b) i) (−3, 1)   **ii)** (5, 4)   **iii)** (3, −2)

iv) (1, 1)   **v)** (−4, −3)   **vi)** (4, −3)

Page 161   Exercise 2

1 a) B   **b)** A   **c)** C

2 a) i) C   **ii)** B   **iii)** E   **iv)** D

  b) $y = 3x + 8$

Page 162   Exercise 3

1 a) i) 2   **ii)** (0, 3)   **b) i)** 6   **ii)** (0, 1)

  c) i) 3   **ii)** (0, −4)   **d) i)** 5   **ii)** (0, 0)

  e) i) 1   **ii)** (0, 7)   **f) i)** 1   **ii)** (0, −2)

  g) i) −2   **ii)** (0, 4)   **h) i)** −2   **ii)** (0, 4)

  i) i) 0   **ii)** (0, 6)

2 a) $y = x - 2$ and $y = 3 + x$ (both have gradient = 1)

  b) $y = 2x + 2$ and $y = 2 + 3x$ (both have y-intercept = 2)

3 a) $y = 4x + 1$ **b)** $y = 2x - 3$

  c) $y = -2x + 5$ ($y = 5 - 2x$)   **d)** $y = x$

Section 13 — Angles and Shapes

13.1   2D Shapes

Page 163   Exercise 1

1 a) 5 lines

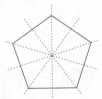

  b) 2 lines

  c) 3 lines

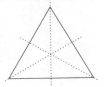

d) 1 line

e) 0 lines

f) 1 line

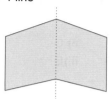

2　a) 4 lines

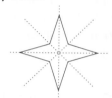

b) 2 lines

c) 1 line

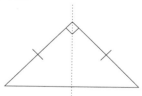

3　a)

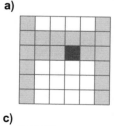

b)

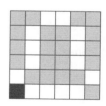

c)

d)

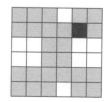

4

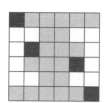

Page 165　Exercise 2

1　a) 4　　　　**b)** 1　　　　**c)** 8
　　d) 2　　　　**e)** 1　　　　**f)** 5
2　a) 3　　　　**b)** 2　　　　**c)** 1
3　a)

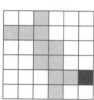

b)

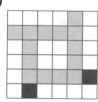

Page 167　Exercise 3

1　a) Equilateral　　**b)** Isosceles　　**c)** Scalene

2　a) i)

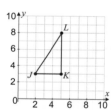

ii) Right-angled

b) i)

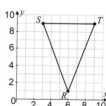

ii) Isosceles

c) i)

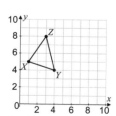

ii) Scalene

3

Sketch	Name of triangle	Number of lines of symmetry	Order of rotational symmetry
E.g.	Scalene	0	1
E.g.	Equilateral	3	3
	Isosceles	1	1

4 a) Isosceles   **b)** Scalene or right-angled

5 $x = 60$, $y = 75$, $z = 6$, $r = 90$,

6 Yes – a right-angled isosceles triangle has one angle of 90° and the other two angles the same size as each other (45°).

Page 169   Exercise 4

1 a) Parallelogram   **b)** Trapezium   **c)** Kite
   d) Square   **e)** Rectangle   **f)** Rhombus

2

Sketch	Name of quadrilateral	Number of lines of symmetry	Order of rotational symmetry
E.g.	Trapezium	0	1
E.g.	Square	4	4
	Rectangle	2	2
E.g.	Kite	1	1
E.g.	Rhombus	2	2
	Parallelogram	0	2

3 $a = 54$
    $b = 8$
    $c = 111$

4 a) Kite
   b) Kite, Parallelogram, Square, Rectangle, Rhombus
   c) Rectangle, Rhombus
   d) Parallelogram, Rectangle, Rhombus

13.2   Properties of 3D Shapes

Page 171   Exercise 1

1 a) i) 6   **ii)** 8   **iii)** 12
   b) i) 5   **ii)** 5   **iii)** 8
   c) i) 5   **ii)** 6   **iii)** 9

2 a) Square-based Pyramid, Regular Tetrahedron, Triangular Prism
   b) Cone, Cylinder, Regular Tetrahedron, Sphere
   c) Cube, Cuboid
   d) Sphere

3 A, C, E and F are prisms

4   Regular Tetrahedron

5   7 faces, 10 vertices and 15 edges

13.3   Angle Rules

Page 173   Exercise 1

1 a) $a = 180° - 140° = 40°$
   b) $b = 360° - 280° = 80°$
   c) $c = 90° - 50° = 40°$

2 a) 50°   **b)** 65°   **c)** 11°

3 a) 80°   **b)** 30°   **c)** 169°

4 a) 65°   **b)** 50°   **c)** 34°

5 a) 285°   **b)** 150°   **c)** 130°

6 a) 155°   **b)** 65°   **c)** 96°

7 p and q, r and s

Page 175   Exercise 2

1 a) d and f, e and g
   b) k and i, h and j
   c) l and n, m and o

2 a) 100°   **b)** 160°   **c)** 88°

3 a) $a = 25°$, $b = 155°$, $c = 155°$
   b) $d = 110°$, $e = 70°$, $f = 70°$
   c) $g = 123°$, $h = 57°$, $i = 57°$
   d) $j = 63°$, $k = 117°$, $l = 63°$
   e) $m = 143°$, $n = 37°$, $p = 143°$
   f) $q = 141°$, $r = 39°$, $s = 39°$

4   E.g.

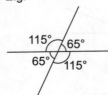

Page 177   Exercise 1

1 **a)** $x = 180° - 85° - 20° = 75°$
   b) $t = 180° - 115° - 40° = 25°$
   c) $e = 180° - 70° - 62° = 48°$
   d) $p = 180° - 25° - 22° = 133°$
   e) $j = 180° - 65° - 65° = 50°$
   f) $z = 180° - 78° - 41° = 61°$

2 **a)** 25°   **b)** 60°   **c)** 82°
   d) 65°   **e)** 60°   **f)** 68°

3 **a)** 40°   **b)** 70°   **c)** 45°

Page 179   Exercise 2

1 **a)** $a = 360° - 175° - 55° - 25° = 105°$
   b) $b = 360° - 120° - 115° - 60° = 65°$
   c) $c = 360° - 225° - 88° - 31° = 16°$
   d) $d = 360° - 145° - 74° - 29° = 112°$

2 **a)** 125°   **b)** 60°   **c)** 55°
   d) 119°   **e)** 15°   **f)** 124°

3 **a)** $a = 64°, b = 116°$
   b) $c = 104°, d = 52°$
   c) $e = 90°, f = 54°$
   d) $g = 115°, h = 32°$
   e) $i = 109°, j = 71°, k = 71°$
   f) $l = 105°, m = 105°$

4 27°, 153°, 153°

5 $x = 106°, y = 74°, z = 32°$

Section 14 — Constructions

Page 181   Exercise 1

1 **a)** $b = 52$ mm $c = 45$ mm $d = 55°$
   b) $e = 38$ mm $f = 58$ mm $g = 132°$

2 **a)** $x = 38$ mm $y = 53$ mm $z = 53$ mm
      $a = 69°$ $b = 69°$ $c = 42°$
   b) $u = 38$ mm $v = 63$ mm $w = 87$ mm
      $d = 122°$ $e = 37°$ $f = 22°$

3 **a)** $k = 43°$ $l = 317°$
   b) $p = 310°$ $q = 230°$ $r = 310°$
      $s = 230°$

4 **a)** E.g.   **b)** E.g.

  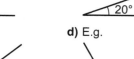

   c) E.g.   **d)** E.g.

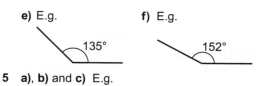

e) E.g.   **f)** E.g.
        135°   152°

5 **a), b)** and **c)** E.g.

45°   60°
9 cm

6 **a), b)** and **c)** E.g.

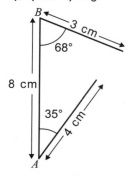

B 3 cm
68°
8 cm
35°
4 cm
A

7 **a), b)** and **c)**

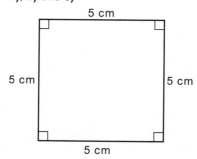

5 cm
5 cm   5 cm
5 cm

   d) square

8 **a)** and **b)**

60 mm   75°
36°
38 mm
62 mm   69°

9 **a)** and **b)**

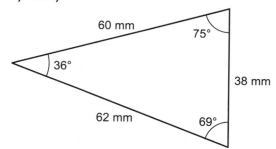

68°   39 mm   29 mm   60°
32 mm   32 mm
232°
90°   90°
62 mm

14.2 Constructing Triangles

Page 184 Exercise 1

1 If you've drawn the triangles accurately you'll find that:
 a) right-angled triangle **b)** isosceles triangle
 c) scalene triangle **d)** isosceles triangle

2 **a)** E.g.

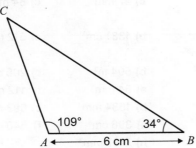

 b) E.g.

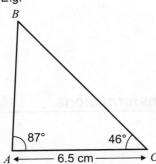

 c) E.g.

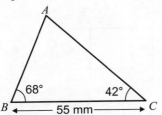

3 If you've drawn the triangles accurately you'll find that:
 a) m = 45 mm n = 25 mm
 b) m = 53 mm n = 42 mm

4 **a)** E.g.

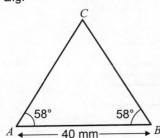

 b) AC = 38 mm BC = 38 mm
 c) isosceles triangle

Page 186 Exercise 2

1 If you've drawn the triangles accurately you'll find that:
 a) 50 mm **b)** 39 mm
 c) 32 mm **d)** 28 mm

2 **a)** E.g.

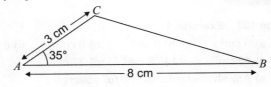

 b) E.g.

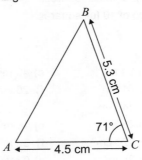

 c) E.g.

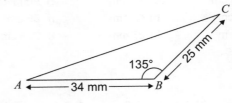

3 **a)** E.g.

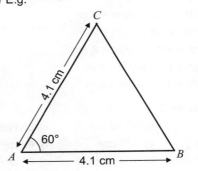

 b) 4.1 cm
 c) equilateral triangle

Section 15 — Perimeter, Area and Volume

15.1 Perimeter

Page 187 Exercise 1

1 **a)** 37 m **b)** 32 m **c)** 38 cm
 d) 43 cm **e)** 43 m **f)** 54 m
2 **a)** 29 cm **b)** 38 cm **c)** 51 m
3 **a)** 14 cm **b)** 20 cm

Page 188 Exercise 2

1 **a)** 8 cm **b)** 16 m **c)** 36 m
 d) 44 cm
2 **a)** 10 cm **b)** 20 m **c)** 26 m
 d) 44 m
3 **a)** 48 cm **b)** 30 cm **c)** 40 m
 d) 40 cm **e)** 34 cm **f)** 28 cm
 g) 22 m **h)** 22 m

15.2 Area

Page 190   Exercise 1

1 a) 6 cm²   **b)** 9 cm²   **c)** 8 cm²   **d)** 8 cm²

2 a) 15 cm²   **b)** 25 cm²   **c)** 27 cm²

3 a) Any shape made up of 5 full squares.

  b) Any shape made up of 9 full squares.

  c) Any shape made up of 10 full squares and 1 half square.

Page 191   Exercise 2

1 a) 16 cm²   **b)** 64 m²   **c)** 49 m²

  d) 121 cm²   **e)** 81 cm²   **f)** 25 cm²

  g) 4 cm²   **h)** 144 m²

2 a) 35 cm²   **b)** 18 m²   **c)** 18 m²

  d) 44 cm²   **e)** 120 cm²   **f)** 32 m²

3 a) 9 cm²   **b)** 28 m²   **c)** 9 m²

  d) 169 cm²   **e)** 70 mm²   **f)** 96 m²

  g) 22 cm²   **h)** 42 cm²   **i)** 66 cm²

  j) 132 m²   **k)** 27 mm²   **l)** 225 cm²

4 196 m²

5 175 m²

6 120 m²

7 a) 6 cm   **b)** 5 cm   **c)** 9 m   **d)** 2 cm   **e)** 1 m

8 a) E.g. length = 6 cm, width = 4 cm

  b) E.g. length = 8 cm, width = 2 cm

  c) E.g. length = 4 cm, width = 3 cm

  d) E.g. length = 5 m, width = 6 m

  e) E.g. length = 7 m, width = 6 m

Page 193   Exercise 3

1 a) 24 m²   **b)** 28 m²   **c)** 83 cm²

  d) 91 cm²   **e)** 120 cm²   **f)** 42 m²

2 a) 114 m²   **b)** 109 cm²   **c)** 81 cm²

3 60 m²

4 1560 m²

Page 195   Exercise 4

1 a) Area $= \dfrac{4 \times 6}{2}$

  Area $= \dfrac{24}{2}$

  Area = 12 cm²

  b) Area $= \dfrac{5 \times 10}{2}$

  Area $= \dfrac{50}{2}$

  Area = 25 cm²

2 a) Area $= \dfrac{10 \times 11}{2}$

  Area = 55 m²

  b) Area $= \dfrac{9 \times 12}{2}$

  Area = 54 m²

3 a) 10 cm²   **b)** 9 cm²   **c)** 45 m²   **d)** 66 m²

  e) 24 m²   **f)** 18 m²   **g)** 21 cm²   **h)** 44 m²

4 a) 36 m²   **b)** 15 cm²   **c)** 40 m²   **d)** 30 m²

5 60 m²

6 1750 cm²

15.3 Volume

Page 197   Exercise 1

1 a) 8 cm³   **b)** 8 cm³   **c)** 9 cm³

  d) 16 cm³   **e)** 10 cm³   **f)** 13 cm³

Page 198   Exercise 2

1 a) 125 cm³   **b)** 27 mm³   **c)** 64 m³

  d) 729 m³

2 a) 343 mm³   **b)** 1331 cm³   **c)** 512 m³

  d) 1728 cm³

3 a) 126 cm³   **b)** 504 m³   **c)** 200 cm³

  d) 324 m³   **e)** 54 mm³   **f)** 112 cm³

4 a) 275 cm³   **b)** 1584 mm³   **c)** 693 m³

  d) 220 m³   **e)** 396 cm³   **f)** 540 cm³

  g) 792 m³   **h)** 2197 mm³

5 432 cm³

6 400 m³

7 24 000 mm³

8 9000 cm³

Section 16 — Transformations

16.1 Reflection

Page 200   Exercise 1

1 a)

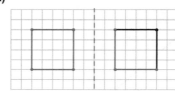

  b)

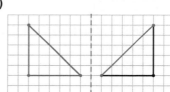

  c)

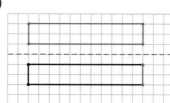

  d)

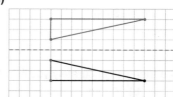

2 a)

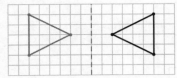

b)

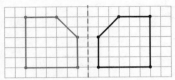

c)

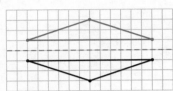

d)

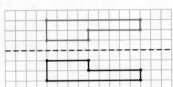

3 a)

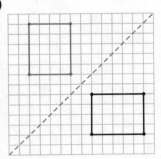

b)

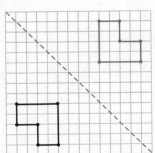

4 a)

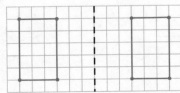

b)

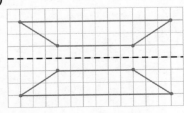

c)

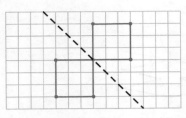

d)

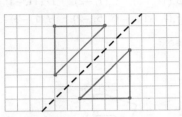

Page 202 Exercise 2

1 a)

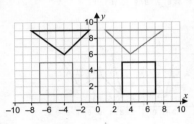

b)

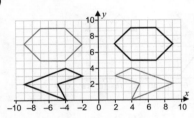

2 a)

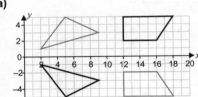

b)

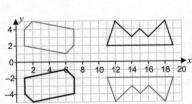

3 a) and b)

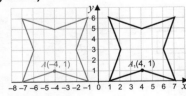

4 a) and b)

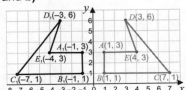

5 a)

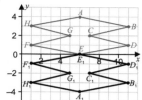

b) $A_1(6, -4)$, $B_1(11, -3)$, $C_1(7, -2)$, $D_1(11, -1)$,
$E_1(6, 0)$, $F_1(1, -1)$, $G_1(5, -2)$, $H_1(1, -3)$

Page 204   Exercise 3

1 a) and **b)**

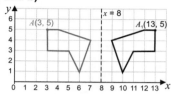

2 a), **b)** and **c)**

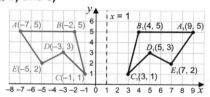

3 a) and **b)**

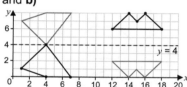

4 a), **b)** and **c)**

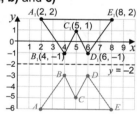

5 a) $x = 7$
  b) $y = 3$

16.2 Rotation

Page 205   Exercise 1

1 a)

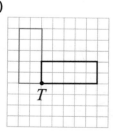

b)

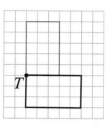

c)

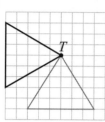

d)

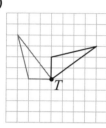

e)

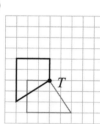

f)

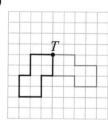

2 a)

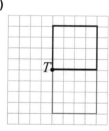

b)

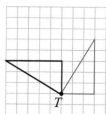

c)

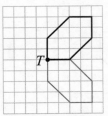

3 a)

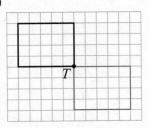

b)

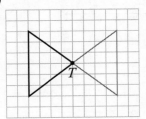

c)

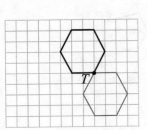

4 a)

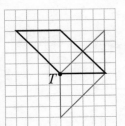

b)

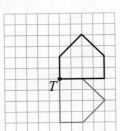

c)

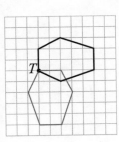

5 a)

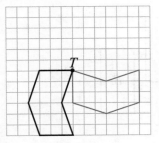

b)

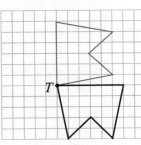

c)

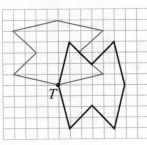

Page 207 Exercise 2

1 a)

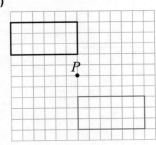

b)

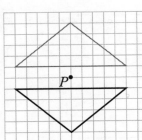

c)

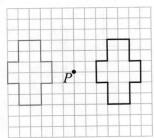

2 a) i) and ii)

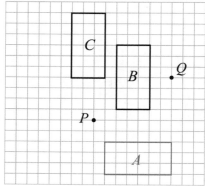

b) i) and ii)

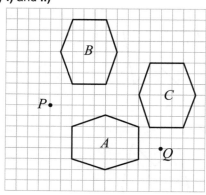

Page 208 Exercise 3

1 a)

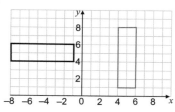

b)

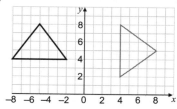

2 a)

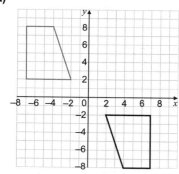

b)

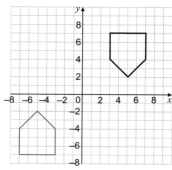

3 a)

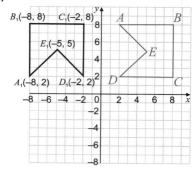

b)

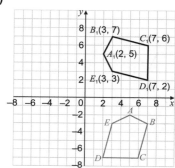

4 a)

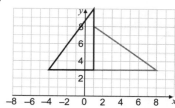

b)

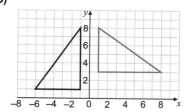

16.3 Translation

Page 210 Exercise 1

1 a)

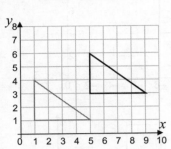

b)

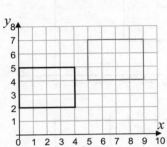

2 a) and b)

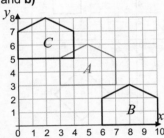

3 a) and b)

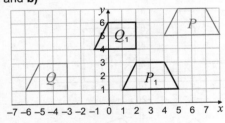

4 a), b), c) and d)

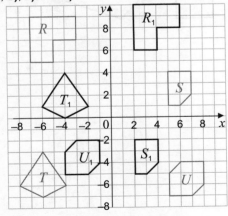

5 a) 5 squares right and 2 squares up

b) 4 squares left and 4 squares up

c) 3 squares left and 4 squares down

6 a) 11 squares right and 12 squares down

b) 11 squares left and 12 squares up

c) 10 squares down

d) 10 squares up

e) 11 squares left and 2 squares up

f) 11 squares right and 2 squares down

16.4 Enlargement

Page 212 Exercise 1

1 a) E.g.

b) E.g.

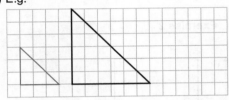

c) E.g.

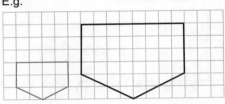

d) E.g.

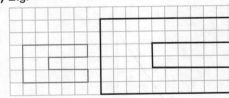

2 a) E.g.

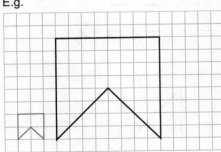

b) E.g.

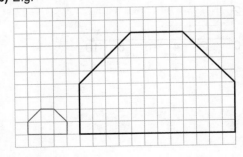

3 Measure your drawings to make sure they have these dimensions:

a)

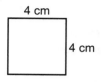

4 cm
4 cm

b)

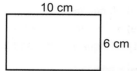

10 cm
6 cm

c)

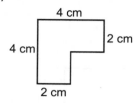

4 cm
2 cm
4 cm
2 cm

4 Side length = 42 cm

5 Base length = 24 cm   Height = 80 cm

Page 214   Exercise 2

1 a)

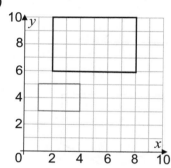

b)

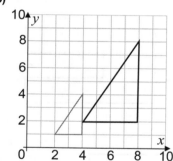

c)

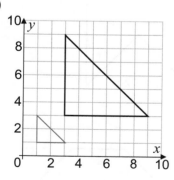

2 a)

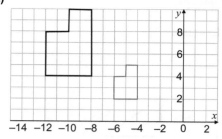

b)

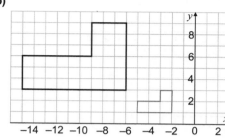

3 a)

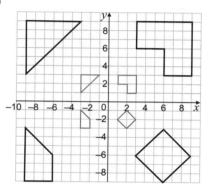

b)

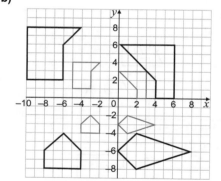

Section 17 — Probability

17.1 The Probability Scale

Page 216   Exercise 1

1 1. You will grow a third arm.
3. Someone you know will win a car this week.
2. You will eat something tomorrow.

2 **a)** impossible   **b)** certain   **c)** unlikely
d) even   **e)** even   **f)** likely

3 **a)** B   **b)** C   **c)** D   **d)** A

4

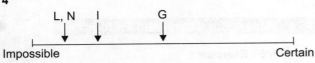

5 **a)** D   **b)** A   **c)** B   **d)** C
6 **a)** C   **b)** A   **c)** B   **d)** D
7

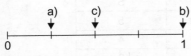

17.2 Probability Experiments

Page 218   Exercise 1

1 **a)** $\frac{17}{50}$ **b)** $\frac{33}{50}$

2 1: 49%, 2: 34%, 3: 8%, 4: 9%

3 E.g. 1: $\frac{26}{130}$, 2: $\frac{21}{130}$, 3: $\frac{18}{130}$, 4: $\frac{31}{130}$, 5: $\frac{19}{130}$, 6: $\frac{15}{130}$

4 **a) i)** $\frac{9}{50}$ **ii)** $\frac{9}{25}$

b) $\frac{2}{5}$

5 **a)** $\frac{3}{5}$ **b)** 60%   **c)** 0.6

6 1: $\frac{23}{100}$, 0.23, 23%   2: $\frac{27}{100}$, 0.27, 27%

3: $\frac{19}{100}$, 0.19, 19%   4: $\frac{41}{200}$, 0.205, 20.5%

5: $\frac{21}{200}$, 0.105, 10.5%

17.3 Theoretical Probabilities

Page 220   Exercise 1

1 **a)** 10   **b)** 6   **c)** $\frac{3}{5}$
2 **a)** 6

b) i) $\frac{1}{6}$ **ii)** $\frac{1}{3}$ **iii)** $\frac{1}{2}$

3 $\frac{1}{4}$

4 **a)** $\frac{1}{6}$ **b)** 3   **c)** $\frac{1}{2}$

5 **a)** $\frac{1}{13}$ **b)** $\frac{1}{2}$ **c)** $\frac{1}{4}$

6 **a)** $\frac{1}{4}$ **b)** $\frac{1}{4}$ **c)** 0   **d)** $\frac{3}{4}$ **e)** $\frac{1}{2}$

Page 222   Exercise 2

1 0.4

2 **a)** 0.1   **b)** 0.8

3 15%

4 0.34

5 **a)** $\frac{2}{5}$ **b)** $\frac{3}{5}$

6 **a)** 0.35, 35%, $\frac{7}{20}$ **b)** 0.6, 60%, $\frac{3}{5}$

7 **a)** $\frac{13}{20}$ **b)** $\frac{17}{20}$ **c)** $\frac{9}{20}$

Page 223   Exercise 3

1 E.g.

Coin	H	H	H	H	T	T	T	T
Spinner	1	2	3	4	1	2	3	4

2 E.g.

Card	Red	Red	Red	Black	Black	Black
Spinner	1	2	3	1	2	3

3 **a)** E.g.

Bag 1	Bag 2
Strawberry	Lime
Strawberry	Apple
Lemon	Lime
Lemon	Apple
Orange	Lime
Orange	Apple

b) 6

4 **a)** 8   **b)** 2   **c)** $\frac{1}{4}$

5 **a)** E.g.

Spin 1	Spin 2
Red	Red
Red	Yellow
Red	Green
Red	Blue
Yellow	Red
Yellow	Yellow
Yellow	Green
Yellow	Blue
Green	Red
Green	Yellow
Green	Green
Green	Blue
Blue	Red
Blue	Yellow
Blue	Green
Blue	Blue

b) 16   **c)** 7   **d)** $\frac{7}{16}$

6 a) E.g.

Morning	Afternoon
Tennis	Hiking
Tennis	Canoeing
Tennis	Cycling
Swimming	Hiking
Swimming	Canoeing
Swimming	Cycling
Football	Hiking
Football	Canoeing
Football	Cycling

b) $\frac{1}{3}$ **c)** $\frac{1}{9}$

7 a) E.g.

Spin 1	Spin 2
1	1
1	2
1	3
1	4
2	1
2	2
2	3
2	4
3	1
3	2
3	3
3	4
4	1
4	2
4	3
4	4

b) $\frac{1}{16}$ **c)** $\frac{1}{4}$

Page 225   Exercise 4

1

	1	2	3	4
Heads	H1	H2	H3	H4
Tails	T1	T2	T3	T4

2

	Red	Orange	Green
Red	RR	RO	RG
Orange	OR	OO	OG
Green	GR	GO	GG

3 a)

	2	4	6	8
1	3	5	7	9
2	4	6	8	10
3	5	7	9	11
4	6	8	10	12

b) 16

Section 18 — Statistics

18.1 Tables, Bar Charts and Pictograms

Page 226   Exercise 1

1 a)

Season	Frequency
Spring	5
Summer	5
Autumn	4
Winter	6

   b) 20   **c)** 11

2 a) 40   **b)** 4

   c) 28   **d)** Brown

3 a) 25   **b)** 6

   c) 17   **d)** 1

   e) 16%   **f)** 32%

Page 228   Exercise 2

1 a)

Speed (mph)	Tally	Frequency
21-25	III	3
26-30	IIII	4
31-35	HHI	5
36-40	IIII	4
41-45	III	3
46-50	I	1

   b) 20   **c)** 7   **d)** 4

2 a) 100   **b)** 46

   c) 24%   **d)** 60%

3 a) 60   **b)** 60%   **c)** 76-100

   d) i) 150

     ii) The data is grouped, so you don't know the exact number of calls each day.

Page 229   Exercise 3

1

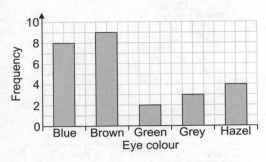

2

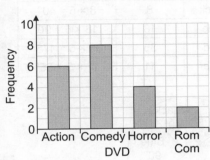

3

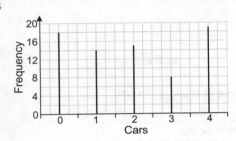

4

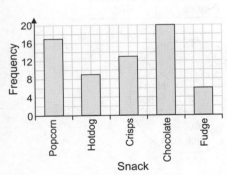

5

Favourite Subject	Frequency
Art	14
Music	16
Maths	4
French	10
Science	5

6 a) 35   **b)** 15   **c)** size 5

Page 231   Exercise 4

1

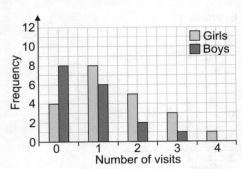

2 a) 14   **b)** January and April
   c) 1   **d)** 57
3 a) Tim   **b)** 22 miles
   c) 8 miles   **d)** Stuart
4 a)

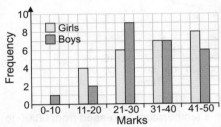

b) 44%
c) E.g. Yes, the graph shows that more girls than boys got the highest marks.

Page 233   Exercise 5

1

Jan	👕 👕 👕 👕
Feb	👕 👕 👕 🙂
Mar	👕 👕

2

Sept	👤 👤 👤 👤 👤
Oct	👤 👤 👤 👤 👤 👤 👤
Nov	👤 👤 👤 👤 👤
Dec	👤 👤 👤 👤

3

Tennis	⬡ ⬡
Football	⬡ ⬡ ⬡
Rugby	⬡ ◿
Athletics	◿

4 a) 65   **b)** 165   **c)** 55   **d)** $\frac{5}{22}$
5 a) 20   **b)** 12   **c)** 40%
6 a) 2   **b)** Josie   **c)** Ralph   **d)** 20%

Page 235   Exercise 1

1

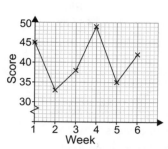

2 a)

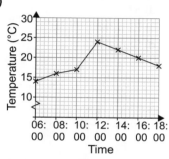

b) 08:00 and 10:00

c) E.g. the temperature increased from 06:00 to 12:00, reaching the highest value of 24 °C at 12:00. From 12:00, the temperature decreased to 18 °C at 18:00.

3 a) £6500   b) 4 years

  c) £200   d) Year 0 and Year 1

4 a) July   b) 6400   c) 2400

  d) E.g the number of visitors increased from March to July, reaching the highest value of 9000 visitors in July. From July to October, the number of visitors decreased steeply, falling to 2600 by October.

Page 237   Exercise 1

1 Drama

2 a) Chocolate   b) Mint

3 a) Ham   b) $\frac{1}{6}$ c) 120

4 a) Dog   b) Fish   c) $\frac{2}{9}$

  d) No – the pie chart just gives proportions, and not actual numbers.

5 a) Rock and jazz   b) $\frac{1}{3}$ c) 12

6 a) $\frac{7}{18}$ b) 35   c) 105

Page 239   Exercise 2

1 a) 10°

  b)

Colour	Frequency	Angle
Brown	15	15 × 10 = 150°
Blonde	17	17 × 10 = 170°
Other	4	4 × 10 = 40°

c)

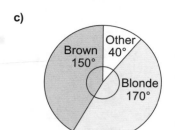

2 a) 72   b) 5°

  c)

Colour	Frequency	Angle
Black	8	8 × 5 = 40°
Blue	18	18 × 5 = 90°
Red	35	35 × 5 = 175°
Other	11	11 × 5 = 55°

  d)

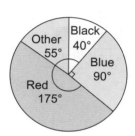

3 a) 18   b) 20°

  c)

Type of Book	Angle
Fiction	200°
Non-fiction	100°
Picture	60°

  d)

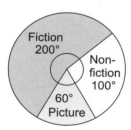

4 a) 72

  b)

Number of Pets	Angle
0	180°
1	110°
2	50°
3 or more	20°

  c)

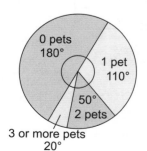

5

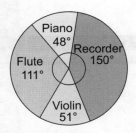

Piano 48°
Recorder 150°
Flute 111°
Violin 51°

18.4 Correlation

Page 241   Exercise 1

1 a) Negative correlation
   b) Positive correlation
   c) No correlation

2 a) Negative correlation. As the mileage of a car increases, its value decreases.
   b) No correlation. There is no connection between a person's shoe size and how much time they spend reading each day.
   c) Positive correlation. The longer the race distance, the greater the world record time to complete it.

3 a) Graph **i)**. Positive correlation — people with large feet are likely to also have large hands.
   b) Graph **i)**. Positive correlation — people are more likely to visit a theme park if the temperature is higher.
   c) Graph **iii)**. No correlation — there probably isn't a connection between the wind speed and how many newspapers are bought.
   d) Graph **i)**. Positive correlation — people who spend longer revising are likely to do well on a science test.
   e) Graph **ii)**. Negative correlation — the more time people spend watching TV, the less time they will have available for doing homework.

18.5 Averages and Range

Page 243   Exercise 1

1 7

2 a) 1, 2, 2, 3, 5, 8
   b) 7

3 Mode = 6, Range = 6

4 a) i) 7   **ii)** 7
   b) i) 23   **ii)** 12
   c) i) 1   **ii)** 9
   d) i) 11   **ii)** 1
   e) i) 52   **ii)** 19
   f) i) 46   **ii)** 38
   g) i) 94   **ii)** 17
   h) i) 123   **ii)** 88

5 £7.49

6 a) 6   **b)** 32

7 a) 67   **b)** 10

Page 245   Exercise 2

1 9

2 a) 9, 10, 11, 14, 15, 16, 19   **b)** 14

3 a) 14   **b)** 42   **c)** 18   **d)** 8
   e) 2   **f)** 22   **g)** 86   **h)** 106

4 a) 5, 6, 6, 8, 11, 12   **b)** 6, 8   **c)** 7

5 a) 13   **b)** 4   **c)** 6
   d) 17   **e)** 45   **f)** 61

6 22

7 97 books

Page 246   Exercise 3

1 a) 25   **b)** 5

2 a) 6   **b)** 4   **c)** 8   **d)** 12   **e)** 15
   f) 12   **g)** 18   **h)** 22   **i)** 52   **j)** 24

3 a) 6.5   **b)** 9.5   **c)** 7.8   **d)** 22.6
   e) 29.8   **f)** 56.5   **g)** 3.6   **h)** 20.5

4 88p

5 24

6 150 g

7 30 °C

8 a) 20 cm   **b)** 19 cm

Page 248   Exercise 4

1 The boys have bigger shoe sizes than the girls.

2 In general, it was warmer in Wick than in Bouth over the month.

3 The red team had a larger variation in the number of points they scored. / The blue team had more consistent scores.

4 In general, the dogs were heavier than the cats. / The weights of the cats were more consistent.

M1NA31

£2.00
(Retail Price)

www.cgpbooks.co.uk

Mathematics for **Key Stage Three**